# If Trees Could Talk:

## Life Lessons from the Wisdom of the Woods

### ∾ A COMPANION WORKBOOK ∾

## HOLLY WORTON

TRIBAL PUBLISHING

# If Trees Could Talk:
# Life Lessons from the Wisdom of the Woods
## ∽ A COMPANION WORKBOOK ∽

Holly Worton Tribal Publishing Ltd
Copyright © 2019 by Holly Worton

ISBN 978-1-911161-27-1

Interior design by Esther Lemmens at Zesty Books
www.zestybooks.co.uk

# Table of Contents

# PART
## ONE

# Introduction

I truly hope that you enjoyed my book *If Trees Could Talk: Life Lessons from the Wisdom of the Woods*. When I wrote the book, it was not meant to be something that you simply leaf through from the comfort of your home; it was meant to be a very experiential book. I hope to encourage people to get outdoors more in whatever way they can and to engage with Nature however they choose to do so. The trees did a fantastic job of sharing incredibly simple activities to help people connect more with Nature.

In the interest of making it as easy as possible for you to experience these activities, I've created this workbook. It contains the original tree stories, a recap of the actions they suggested that we take, and a list of journal prompts. Most importantly, it's got space for you to make your own notes and record your own observations about your experiences.

As a reminder, I've also created a little online space with guided meditations and other materials that will help you to work through some of these activities. You can access these free resources by going to **http://hollyworton.com/trees**.

Finally, if you do decide to write about your relationship with Nature or your experiences with any of these activities, please reach out to me and let me know. I'd love to hear from you. You can use the contact form on my website: **http://hollyworton.com/contact**.

# How to Use this Workbook

How you use this workbook is entirely up to you, and you alone will know the best way for you to work through the chapters based on what's right for *you*. *You're* the one who is actually going to do the work here. Be sure to tailor this to fit your own personal wants and needs.

Remember: in this book, as in life, only *you* know what's best for you. Take any advice you receive with a grain of salt, including the suggestions in this book. Take what serves you; leave what doesn't. Likewise, some of what's shared in this workbook will resonate with you, some of it may not. See what feels right to you and go from there. Some topics may require a stretch outside of your comfort zone; others may require you to expand your current belief system. *You do you.*

You can use this workbook in a variety of ways:

* Read each chapter in order and experience the adventure in chronological order
* Dip in and out as you like
* Open the book at a random point and read the chapter that you open up to
* Pick one species of tree and read through all the oak stories, then all the yew stories, then the sycamore stories
* Read through the table of contents and pick whichever chapter stands out to you

Do not be bothered if you cannot find oaks, yews, and sycamores in your local region. You do not need to replicate my experiences, nor do you need to seek out the same species of trees.

All trees have wisdom. All trees will help you to connect to the magical healing powers of Nature. Do what you can with what you have available to you in your local area. But I urge you: do not simply read. *Do. Be. Experience.* I wish you the best of luck on your journey!

Are you ready? Let's get started.

# PART
# TWO

# LONE OAK

Once upon a time, this was a natural forest, a native forest. A forest of mixed evergreens and deciduous trees, and we all lived in peace and quiet and silence. It was a kind of natural harmony.

There were local people here in this area, people who would occasionally walk through this forest, down the trails that you see today. And sometimes one would stop and have a meal underneath my boughs. They would rest up against my trunk, and then they would move on. This was a peaceful wood.

It is no longer so: now you hear the roar of the chainsaw off in the distance. That sound came to us, and my friends — my family — were cut down to make way for an evergreen forest. Not a forest really, but a plantation. A plantation of trees, a colony of trees, made up of just one kind of tree.

For some reason they let me stay. They cut down the trees all around me — my network, my family — and planted these evergreens, the ancestors of those which you see today. The diversity of our community was gone.

I do not begrudge my new neighbors — it was not their fault. It was not their hand that cut the native forest. And they are beautiful, as all trees are: green all year round, lush undergrowth, tiny trees at the base, and straight, naked, trunks. It is a pleasant view. Although I miss my friends from long ago, I understand that your culture may need these trees, may need these products, and may need this work to be carried out.

It feels unnatural, though. They grow so straight that it saddens me because this is not a forest. It is simply a field of trees, a hillside of trees. You may hear a pheasant off in the distance, smaller birds chirping up high. There is life here, but not like there used to be.

People often say that if the trees could talk, what stories they'd tell. And we have stories, we do have stories....

Humans want things to happen quickly, but in the world of the trees, life is slow, life is long, at least for those of us who are natural trees, native trees. The ones who have been planted here will be harvested, just like another crop, as if they were a field of wheat, or oats, or rye. They will be gone, and the field will be empty until new trees are planted. It is slow, and it is long, and it is a peaceful process...until harvest time comes again. And every time they come to cut the trees, I fear that I will be included, that I will be seen as a nuisance, or that I will be struck by one of the falling trees and damaged, and so they decide to take me out, too.

Life isn't what it was back then, back when this was a native forest.

I am aware that perhaps this was not the story that you wanted to hear. Perhaps you wanted something quaint, and pretty; something heart-warming, something funny. Other trees will have those stories for you, not I. For I cannot forget my friends, my family, and my network. I cannot deny the fact that I am one of a kind here in this field of trees. Up here on the hillside; alone, yet not alone. Surrounded by trees that are not like me.

You may not want to include my story in your book at all; you may not want to put it at the beginning, as one of the first stories, even though I am the first tree that you are talking to. Mine is not a light-hearted tale. And yet this story needs to be told.

People know about commercial forests, as they call them, people know about these fields of trees, not native; and yet, they have not heard the story from the tree's perspective. People walk down these paths and they say: "How beautiful, an evergreen forest", and they might even see me as they look off to the side, down the path, and notice that I am different. They might be surprised that I am one of a kind, but most do not look. Most of the people who walk through this field of trees in these times, they keep their eyes on the path, chatting amongst themselves, having their own conversations, deeply engaged with each other and not really connecting with the world around them, with the path, with what lies on both sides of the path; with the trees, the birds — birds are simply background noise to them, a pretty song. Or they might not even hear the birds, so engrossed they may be in their conversations.

But if they were to stop, and sit on a fallen log or with their back up against a tree and close their eyes, they could hear the life that is in the woods: the little birds chirping, the pheasants getting startled by something...the slight hum of the cars off in the distance. There are no roads through here, but we can hear your vehicles. It is like a hum that never ends. Your airplanes flying above, mingled with the pheasants calling out to each other, the rustling of the leaves, the fronds of the evergreens as the wind blows a little bit.

They might open their eyes and see the blue sky and the white clouds, just barely visible in between the branches of the evergreens up above. But to see all these things, and to hear all these things, it is necessary to stop, to sit, to be still, to experience the woods, to experience this field of trees, as I call it. For there is so much here — so much going on. If only you would stop and sit and allow your ears to open up to the sounds, and your eyes to look all around you, and take in what appears to be a very still, very quiet place.

This is experiencing the woods; this is experiencing the forest. And yet most people simply walk on by, walk down the trail, walk down the path. This trail is simply a means to get to their destination, and yet the journey in itself has so much. It has so much to offer.

And so, I would like to suggest to those who hear my story: the next time they find themselves out in the woods, or even in a park — the next time they find themselves outdoors in Nature — to sit, to be still, to take in the sounds, both human-made and Nature-made. The roar of an airplane overhead can feel so jarring, but it is part of this world that we are in today, a world that did not exist when I first came to be. But it is the world we are in right now.

Trees. Birds. Leaves.

Sit, and be still, and pay attention. Open your ears, open your eyes; this is experiencing Nature with all your senses; reach out and touch a leaf, a branch...the ground, the soil...the earth...the bark of a tree. We love being touched. We love it when people make contact with us. We like to engage; we like to interact. We must wait for you to come to us. And it so rarely happens. We should be used to it by now, but still, it surprises us. In the same way that two humans would like a hug — or a dog, or a cat, would like to be stroked — we too like contact, touch. Feel the texture of our bark and say hello as you walk by. Not to every tree in the forest, we don't expect that. But we are all individuals just as you are, we all have personalities, although you cannot usually tell this if you are just walking quickly through the woods. We each have a life. We are each a living being, though we do not have a face, though we do not talk with voices out loud as you do. We are all individuals, just as you are. And we long for connection — interaction — not just among ourselves, but with people.

If you were to speak with each of the trees in this tree-field, or in a forest, in a wood, you would get different stories, you would get different voices. You would get different personalities. People look at a forest, especially a commercial forest, like this — a tree-field — and they think that they are all the same, that we are all the same. I am different, of course, to the human eye but my neighbors look like copies of the same tree, though they are each living individuals. Each with a voice, each with a story, these — my neighbors — are young, unlike me. But they have stories, they have voices, and they are each as unique as each of you humans, although they may look similar, although they may even look the same to you.

This is what I wish to share with you. There is diversity in sameness. Even if we look the same, we are different. Some trees would look at humans and say they all look the same, but you know that you do not. You are not the same; you are different, just as we are.

You are cold. It is time for you to go; you can always come back for more....

# Experience

Go to the woods, or to a place in Nature. Stop, sit, be still, and experience the place: open your ears, open your eyes, touch the things around you, smell them. Take in all the sounds that you hear: both human-made and Nature-made.

Use this workbook to write down everything that you see, hear, smell, and feel.

Touch the trees when you're out walking; make physical contact as you greet them.

Pay attention to the differences between the trees in the forest: the different yews, the different oaks, the different hollies (or whatever types of trees you have in your area). How does the energy of each one feel? How is each one different from the others? Were you able to get a sense of their different personalities? Their individuality?

# Journal Prompts

## Before the Experience

* Do you spend much time outdoors in Nature?

* Do you go on walks in Nature, or do you spend quiet time sitting outside?

* Do you usually find yourself moving through Nature, or being still in Nature?

* Do you ever stop and take the time to really observe all the sounds of the outdoors?

* If you were to plan an excursion somewhere where you could sit in stillness in Nature, where would you go? To a park or to a woodland? Or somewhere else, like a river, a lake, or an ocean?

* Do you prefer cozy, closed-in views like the ones you get in a forest, or do you prefer expansive views like you can find on the coast?

* Can you identify the different species of trees in your area? Would you like to be able to do this, maybe by purchasing a guidebook to trees in your area?

* Do you ever stop to notice the differences between the individual trees of each species and compare two oaks or two yews, for example?

## After the Experience

* What human-made sounds did you hear?

* What Nature-made sounds did you hear?

* Did you notice more sounds when you were sitting still in the woods compared to when you were walking?

* How did you feel when you were listening for the sounds?

* Did you hear anything that you couldn't recognize?

* How did you feel when you touched the trees as you greeted them?

* Did it make you feel more connected to the plant life around you?

* What did you notice when comparing different trees of the same species?

* How did they differ? How were they similar?

* Did you have a favorite species or individual tree? Why?

* How did you feel when you were doing this activity?

* Is this something that you'd like to do again?

# CHALICE WELL YEWS

**W**e are not so old as to remember the days when the people still worshipped the gods and the goddesses; when this land really was a sacred place and was seen by all as a place of pilgrimage. But we have heard the stories. We have heard the stories from our ancestors because, you see, we trees have a network: a network that interconnects all of us in a region. And in the same way that you humans pass stories down from grandparents, to children, to grandchildren, to great-grandchildren, we too pass our stories down, from generation to generation of trees. And this is how you will have access to some of the older stories that we have.

These are stories that are stored in the network of all of us trees. The network is there — available — for each of us to pick up, to learn from, to treasure; and to keep the stories alive in the network, to pass them on to future generations.

I am a yew. I am an old yew, but not as old as we can get. You may have seen ancient, ancient yews; hundreds and hundreds of years old. More than a thousand, more than 1,500 years old — we are long-lived trees. And so, our memories in the network can reach far back — and we have much to contribute in keeping these stories alive across generations.

This land that you are on has always been considered sacred. People come here now, and all they see are pretty gardens: a place to come as tourists. They might feel a sense of relaxation here, but it is not until they sit, still and quiet, on a bench by the water, or with their back up against one of our trees, that they can slip into that deep, deep state of relaxation. The worries and the stress of their day-to-day lives slip away, and they are able to sense — a deep sense — of just how special this place is. It is the relaxation that is the sign for them because it is perhaps a sensation that they have not felt before, or that they rarely feel. And this is the sign to them that this is a sacred place, that this is a special place.

But, as I said, not everyone feels this, not everyone senses this. In fact, few people do.

The tourists, the people who are rushing through, completing a quick circuit of the gardens, on their way onto their next tourist stop, perhaps to go shopping in town on the High Street...they will not sense this. They might even be confused as to why it was recommended that they come here: at first glance, it is just a garden, a small ten-acre garden, well taken care of, well-loved by the people who do know just how special this land is. But even those who do not sense the energy here, or the spirits of this land, or the sacredness, they will still take away a seed, a small seed of this sacredness, a small seed of this experience: a small seed that may germinate in the future, or it may sit dormant in their soul, in their minds, in their being, for years...years...years. Until it may germinate, or not.

It is not necessary that everyone recognize the specialness of this place. What is important is that they come here, even as fast-paced tourists, because they will carry that seed. And perhaps they will recommend it to others...and perhaps they will not. But the more people that come here, the more people will experience this and take away a bit of this energy with them, wherever they go, when they return to their normal lives.

A bit of magic — like fairy dust, you might call it. There is no actual dust, of course: it is that sparkle of an energy of the sacredness of this land, of the water, of the spring, of the twin springs. You sense this. Many do.

And when you come to places where you sense this special energy, this special feeling of relaxation, this special feeling of goodness, we would recommend that you sit still, and you bathe in the energy. You can meditate if you know how to do so. Or simply sit, eyes opened, eyes closed, whatever works for you. And we would recommend that you take in — that you bathe in — the magic of this place or of places like this. Once you have felt that feeling, you will be able to recognize it in other places, even other places which you may not know to be sacred, which you may not know to be special, but you will recognize this feeling — it is like a kindred sensation.

We know that the other tree has told you to sit and be still. You may feel frustrated that you are hearing a similar suggestion here. This may be a message that you hear often from us trees because as you know this is something that we are very good at, as we are not mobile like you humans.

We sit. We stand. And we are still.

Not completely still of course: our branches move with the wind, our leaves, our fronds...our needles, if we are a pine. There is movement. But we are firmly rooted in one spot, allowing us to bathe in the deep energy of each place, of the place where we are. And so, we are like a sponge: a sponge for this energy. We can absorb it, and we can radiate it out. This is why some people are drawn to trees, especially to trees in these sacred places.

And the two of us here are like twins; we are like a doorway to this special world. A doorway to this sacred place of water, to the sacred spring, the Red Spring...flowing...flowing...you can hear it all the time in the background. You can hear it bubbling to the left, you can hear it bubbling to the right.

And we are very grateful to have been planted here in this garden. This is one of the most beautiful places we could be. Sacred, sacred, sacred spring. Sacred, sacred, water. Sacred energy.

We are happy to be here, and we are happy to welcome: to welcome visitors as we do, standing as sentries in the entrance that leads up to the first bathing pool...and the waterfall beyond...and the fountain beyond that...and the well beyond that. We are a gateway to all the goodness that lies in this garden.

We are happy to be here and we are happy to welcome, always happy to welcome. This is all.

There is more. *(I returned to the yews on the second night of my stay, this time approaching the second of the two.)*

You sometimes see people placing their hands and their head, against my bark — just as you do when you make first contact. Sometimes they do it because they expect to feel something. Or they think that is how they should make contact. It is certainly one way to create a connection with us, this is true. It is an attempt, and we welcome all attempts to connect with us. We welcome human touch when it is kind, when it is gentle, when it is friendly, when it is peaceful...a hand against our bark, a gentle brushing of our leaves.

We welcome these things. We welcome this contact because we know this means that we are more than just scenery to you — part of the landscape — that perhaps you see us as the living beings that we are. Perhaps you do not understand that we are so unique as individuals. Perhaps you do not understand the respect that we deserve, that our lives deserve.

But it helps the connection; it helps to strengthen the connection. It helps open the communication: even if you do not understand what you are receiving, what you are sending, what you are transmitting. We welcome this touch: it is a start. It is a start. All is good.

There is not much we can say to you right now, and yet there is so much we can say to you. But the message that we have for you, the two of us — the two yews — is this: contact. We relish contact, we invite contact.

Go. Speak to my partner.

*(I returned to the first yew; the one I had spoken with on the previous night).*

Welcome. I was feeling a bit neglected. *(I laughed at this).*

As my partner said: we are different, each of us. He and I are different — and each of us is different from all the other yews, all the other trees, all the other plants.

And so...we invite you to get to know each tree as an individual. Start with a certain type of tree, such as us, the yews.

Touch our bark. Smell our bark. Make contact. Sit with your back against our trunks. Walk around each of us in a circle. And repeat with other yews, to sense how different we all are...our shape, our form, our texture, our height, our girth. These are things that are easy for you to see, easy for you to feel, easy for you to sense. Sense our energy, sense how our energy is different. When you have done this, step back and think: that in the same way that we are different physically, we are different energetically, and we are different inside. That our being is different means that our soul is different. We are each different individuals.

We invite you: get to know the yews, get to know the elders, get to know the oaks, get to know the hollies — they are prickly, but you can approach them. Get to know each of the different kinds of trees, but get to know multiple individual trees within each one, within each type of tree. Really sense the difference: the difference between each of you, between each of us...that we are individuals, that sense that we are individuals.

Know this. Feel this. Sense this.

You can see, for example, that I am different from my partner — I am wider than my partner, I am a bigger tree and I have a different form. And yet, we were planted at the same time, we as a pair, we as partners guarding the entrance to this place, one of the entrances to this place.

We welcome you to sense us, to feel us, to connect with us, to communicate with us. And to those of you who think that you cannot communicate with us — we invite you to see, hear, feel. For these things you can do, these things you know how to do. These things you absolutely can experience, even if you think that you cannot talk to trees; or that you can talk to trees but cannot hear our answers. Communication comes in so many forms, so many forms. And we invite you: see us...hear us...feel us...touch us...smell us. Use your senses to connect with us.

This is communication. Not all communication must be verbal. Not all communication must be verbal, I repeat this. You humans rely very much on verbal connection, on verbal communication; but there are other types of communication that are even more subtle...that are just as valid, that are just as satisfying, that are just as connective.

And we invite you.

Now return to my partner, for he has parting words.

*(I returned to the other yew).*

Hello again. I could echo all that my partner said, for it is all important. We invite you to start with a tree that has always caught your attention, or with the next tree that you see. We invite you to go out into a park, a wood, anywhere that you can easily connect with a tree; where you can easily see a tree; where you can easily spend just a few minutes alone with a tree.

We understand that you may feel self-conscious: you may think that people will stare at you. Find a quiet place to connect with this tree. A place where perhaps you may not be seen, and allow yourself...allow yourself to connect.

Connect without expectations. Connect with an open mind; connect with an open heart. Connect, connect, connect.

This is all we ask, that you take the first step, just one step and that first step is to connect. To see. To hear. To feel.

That is all.

# Experience

Seek out places that have a "special" sort of energy or go to a place in Nature where you feel drawn to. Sit still, and bathe in the energy of the place. Meditate if you like. Focus on how you feel in this place, so you can recognize this feeling in other places. Remember to give thanks to the place before you leave.

Use this workbook to write down everything that you feel in this space.

Make physical contact with the trees: touch their bark, brush your hand across their leaves. Get to know each tree as an individual: start with one type of tree, such as a yew. Touch its bark, smell its bark, smell the leaves and the ground at its base. Use all your senses to connect with the tree. Hug the tree, sit with your back against it, walk around it in a circle and look at it from all angles.

Repeat with other trees of its type and really sense the difference between each individual within the same species. Repeat the process with other types of trees: oaks, hollies, whatever type of tree you want.

# Journal Prompts

## Before the Experience

🌳 Have you ever visited a place where you felt a very special kind of energy?

🌳 Do you know of any places out in Nature that have a sacred feel to them?

🌳 Have you ever visited these places with the intent to just bathe in the energy, or do you feel like you have to do something special while you're there?

🌳 Is this something you'd like to try? If so, where would you go? List all the places you can think of where you feel a "special" kind of energy.

🌳 How do you know that these places are different?

🌳 How do you feel when you're there? How would you describe the energy?

🌳 Do you ever touch the trees when you're out walking?

🌳 Do you think that making physical contact with the trees might help you to connect better with Nature?

🌳 Have you ever felt like you weren't alone when you were out in Nature, and yet couldn't see anyone else around?

🌳 How does this make you feel? Are you curious, or frightened?

🌳 If you feel uncomfortable when this occurs, what might make you feel more at ease?

## After the Experience

🌳 What was it like to use all your senses to connect with the trees?

🌳 How did you feel during this activity?

🌳 Do you feel a greater sense of closeness to the trees now that you've connected with them in this way?

🌳 What was it like to make physical contact with the trees?

🌳 What have you learned from the experience?

🌳 How often do you actually make physical contact with the trees you pass on your walks, whether it's in a park, in a garden, or in a forest?

🌳 Do you ever touch them? Do you reach out to feel their bark, their leaves, or their fruits?

🌳 How do you feel about making more physical contact with the trees you see?

🌳 Are you able to easily see the different trees as individuals?

🌳 Can you really differentiate between the trees in a woodland, or do they all look the same to you?

# JUNIPER BOTTOM YEWS

Yes, this is a sacred grove.

You felt drawn to our energy as you were walking down the trail, and you saw the little path leading into the clearing in the center of the trees. You sensed that there was a reason you had to step off the trail, not necessarily because you wanted to take a break, but because there was something special here. And yet, you hesitated. You hesitated because this was not on your intended path, and this is a message that I have for you right now: sometimes you are on a path walking through the woods, a literal path, or it could be the path of your life that you are on at any given time.

So, sometimes you are on a path, you have a plan, you are walking down the path, you are trying to get from one place to the other, walking, walking, walking and your eye is caught by something just off the path. It could be off to your right, off to your left, and so you walk off this path...or you do not. You might stand there for a moment hesitating, confused, reluctant: reluctant to step off your path, to step off that well-beaten path, to step off the path that you had planned, the planned path that you were traveling on. You may like plans. You may not like to deviate from the path, but sometimes it is necessary: sometimes it is beneficial, sometimes it can help you see things, experience things that you had not planned, things that are a surprise to you, things that you did not expect.

Like a small clearing in the trees.

It could be something as simple as the small clearing in the trees, a place where you sit with your back up against one of them, one of the cool trees on this hot day. And the coolness of the tree — the smoothness of its bark — is restful, it cools you down, it allows you to relax and recharge and then continue on your path. Or...it could be something else. It could be a discovery of something new. A discovery of something different, a discovery of a new trail, a new path that leads to something unknown, a sense of adventure.

And this is why we are the trees of a grove. This is why we would encourage you to step off the trail that you have planned, step off the path that you have planned, and meander, discover, walk, wander...without knowing where you are going, and see where the path leads you. Pay attention to your gut, to your intuition, to the places to which you are drawn when you are walking along your path: you must be aware. It can be easy to just blindly follow a trail, a path, without really paying attention to what's going on — on either side of the trail.

But when you are aware, when you are walking with your eyes open, with your ears open, with your senses alert, that is when you can easily see the little places where you might veer off the path and discover something new, discover something worthwhile, discover something different — and then allow that sense of adventure to be ignited in your life. So many people live routine, daily lives, with no sense of adventure, no sense of fun, with no sense of joy, with no sense of excitement about what may come: so much routine, so much routine. And yet, it can be so easy to allow the adventure into your life in the same way that if you practice as you walk through the woods, you practice being alert, you practice being aware, and you allow yourself, you give yourself permission to be drawn down these side paths and side trails.

Once you re-train yourself to allow these side trips to happen, then it will be easier for you to do the same in your life and to veer off the plan that you have had for yourself, the path that you are walking, the metaphorical path. It will be easier for you to veer from that path when you see something that catches your eye — something that might give you that sense of adventure, that unexpected adventure of new paths, of new things, and it will be easier for you to follow these intuitive nudges off the main road.

This grove has been here for years and years and years.

Now that you are sitting here with your back up against one of us, you can see the other yews: two straight in front of you, three off to your left and another big one up the hill. We have been here so long, just to the right of the path. And yet so few people come to visit us. So few people come to sit with their back against one of our trunks and to rest in the shade that we offer. So many people walk by without even noticing us, without even seeing us, because they are lost in conversation, not paying attention to the riches, to the sensations, which lie on both sides of the path: the visual riches, the sensual riches. The smell of the trees, of the earth and the flowers — many people miss these things.

And we are aware that other trees have given you this story: this slowing down, of stopping, of resting, of sitting, of listening, of seeing, of hearing, of enjoying, of taking in through your senses all that is around you. And yet, it is something that we can all recommend because we are trees.

We stand here for years and years and years watching the people go by, the birds, the animals... and we stand.

It is precisely because of this immobility of ours that we would recommend that you stray from your path: you do not see all the options that you have available to you — most people do not. Most people miss this tiny little trail, that tiny little trail, that little path that comes off the main path and leads to our grove here. And if you open your eyes, and you open your senses, and you become aware of these little things, it can be life-changing for you: you who are able to walk, you who are able to be mobile, you who are able to walk both physically and metaphorically down a path through your life, experiencing things. This is all about the experience. It is all about the adventure of new experiences, of unexpected experiences.

This is what you crave when it has been a long time since the last time you have done a long-distance trail: it is that adventure of walking somewhere new, of seeing someplace new, of walking and walking and walking and not knowing what exactly is to come. You may have a map, you may have a guidebook with indications of what you will see along the path, but it is the adventure of actually experiencing those things.

And that is why we encourage you to stray from the path so that you can experience that sense of adventure. Take the detour. Take the little trail. And again, we mean this not just literally, but metaphorically.

Be aware — with all your senses. Pay attention to the things that catch you up, and be open to exploring. Be open to giving yourself permission to take the detour.

This is all.

# Experience

Step off the trail you're walking on, or the route you have planned. (Note that in the UK, it's best to try this on open access land, where there are many little trails all around and it's legal for you to step away from the public rights of way.) Discover new things: explore where another path goes. Really see all the options you have available to you.

Follow your intuition. Look beyond the path and pay attention to what's on either side of the trail. Practice being alert, aware.

Cultivate a sense of adventure when you're out in Nature: try new things and new trails. Allow the adventure to enter your life.

# Journal Prompts

## Before the Experience

🍃 Do you consider yourself to be a flexible person?

🍃 Do you find it easy to change plans? Can you easily deviate from your planned path?

🍃 How does it feel when you change your itinerary or stray from your intended path? Does it make you feel out of control, disorganized, or something else?

🍃 If this is something that you find difficult, would you like to be more flexible?

🍃 What about options? Do you usually take the time to see all the options you have available to you, or do you impulsively choose the first that you see?

🍃 How would you feel about taking more time to make your decisions?

🍃 How do you make your decisions: with your head or with your intuition?

🍃 Is your life full of adventure? Would you like to have more adventures in your life? How might you make this happen?

## After the Experience

🍃 How did you feel about veering off from the path you had planned, or the trail you were walking?

🍃 What was it like to explore new trails that you weren't familiar with?

🍃 Was it easy to follow your intuition and try new paths?

🍃 What did you discover when you looked at the things on both sides of the trail?

🍃 What was different about this experience?

🍃 What was it like to be more adventurous in the outdoors?

🍃 What did you do differently?

🍃 What else would you like to experiment with?

🍃 How could you add even more adventure to your time in Nature?

🍃 How could you add even more adventure to other aspects of your life?

*If Trees Could Talk – A Companion Workbook*

# WINDMILL HILL SYCAMORE

Yesterday, when you came, I said that I had a story for you, but not right then; and I know that you were disappointed, and I also know that you understood. I also know that it wasn't until much later that you understood why. You cannot simply — and I say this in the most respectful of ways — you cannot simply walk up to us and ask for the story and expect to receive. Even if we have told you that we have the story, we expect more from you.

We expect contact, communication, time.

You have heard from other trees about the importance of sitting, of being still, of engaging with Nature or observing Nature. Of being silent in Nature. And this is why I would not give you the story yesterday, even if perhaps the weather was better for us to do this yesterday — it is cold today, with a chilling wind — perhaps not the ideal situation in which you would want to receive a story, or in which you would even want to settle down and be still in Nature. And yet, you are protected: sitting in the midst of my trunks for I am a multiple-trunked tree, as you can see. You are protected some, and we are not quite at the top of the hill, so the wind has not hit as strongly as it would if you were up higher.

Some say that I am a portal.

You have heard this yourself. A portal to what? A portal to other dimensions, a portal to the fairy realm, a portal to time travel, a portal to anywhere. You have not yet experienced this; it is not time for you to experience this, but it is possible for you to experience this...not today, but at some point.

You know that this is a special place.

The ancient people here used this hill as a burial ground for a reason — not just because it has a pretty view of all around. The hill was more wooded then; there were more trees, it had not been cleared for farming. And I know this because I retain the history through the network. You know that us trees have a network, but what you may not know is that generations of trees receive the information down the lines. And this is how I know what it was like back then. This is still a peaceful land, still quiet, still not very developed. But it was much more rustic back then, before agriculture had taken on in such large forms as it is today. There were no large herds of sheep grazing in this field, rubbing themselves against the barks of us trees to scratch. You see that the tree next to me has a whole section of its bark free from moss and is covered with strands of wool; it is because the sheep scratch themselves on us, and we are happy to have that type of engagement, that type of contact, that type of communication. We are happy to have living things wandering amongst us, and we are happy to serve as a scratching post!

Many people — well, not so many people — but some people do walk up here to this hill, because it is known as a historical point of interest. And yet very few people wander beyond the mounds, into this wood; which is disappointing, because we would love to have more interaction with the people that come here. In this wood you may feel a special energy, it is the energy of the fey; though you cannot see them, you know that they are here. And you are correct in guessing that that little wooded bit of trail, just to the side of this hill, is also a very special place. You can sense that you are not alone when you walk through that tunnel of green, and it is because you are not alone there.

Us trees see through all the dimensions.

We can see the human dimension and we can see the other dimensions as well; and that's how I know that you are not alone here, as you sit seemingly alone amongst my branches, amongst my trunks. The other dimensions overlap with this one. Sometimes you can see through, and sometimes you cannot. They can see through to yours. And they are always checking you out to see your energy, to see if they might reveal themselves, to see if they might step forth and communicate and step forth and connect, step forth and show themselves to you — they very rarely do this, because they know people do not believe. And they did in years past, hundreds of years past, but not so much now, and so they do not take the risk, which we think is unfortunate, but at the same time we understand; and we do not judge, we do not judge.

But if you sit silently, quietly, respectfully for long enough...and if you put forth the intention that you want to connect with them — in a respectful way — you might be just so lucky as to see them, and you might not see them in the way that you think you might see them. You might see them as clearly as you would see another human being, a solid three-dimensional being. Or you might see a shadow. Or you might see a flicker of movement in the corner of your eye. That is them. Or you might hear a sound — a sound that does not belong to a bird, or a hare, or a sheep — a strange sound. And you might find yourself looking behind and seeing nothing — that is them.

Some of the times that you are walking, when you are walking alone, and you get the sense that there is someone there and then you turn and see no one — that is them. They are coming forth to see you, coming forth to observe you, coming forth to evaluate you; but yet not coming forth strongly enough, confidently enough, visible enough for you to really know that they are there. And that is fine. And that is all right.

I don't know what kind of story you were expecting today.

I know that every tree has given you a different story, but I think it is my responsibility to tell you these things about the unseen realms — the unseen dimensions — so that you can know you are not alone, even if it looks like you are. And this is why humans — particularly small humans, young humans, children — enjoy fairy tales, because they still feel that sense of magic that can exist in the forest, even if as adults they may not believe. And I think that this is our job, you and I, to remind them that if they just opened their minds to the possibility, to the possibility of magic — to let in that magic into their lives — that they might start experiencing it in unexpected ways, in pleasant ways.

But to do this, you must respect.

Respect Nature, respect their world, respect the woods, respect the trees, respect the plants, respect the flowers, and respect the animals. So many people come tromping through the woods as if they were entitled to walk here, because it is a public footpath, and so they walk confidently and boldly through this land as if it was theirs. They step on flowers, they step on plants, and they break tree branches. These are the people who quite possibly will never connect with the unseen realms because they lack respect. Pay attention to where you tread. Pay attention to the soil beneath your feet. The rocks. The stones. The plants. Pay attention to the trees that you pass, the shrubs, and the streams.

Connect, connect, connect, and this will help you to connect with the unseen — because it is there. It is there, even if you think you cannot see it. There is layer upon layer upon layer of dimensions that you can connect with, and that you can benefit from connecting with. And we encourage you to do so. We encourage you to open up to the possibility. We sense that sometimes humans may be worried: what will other people think of us if we believe in magic? If we believe in the faeries? If we believe in the Nature spirits? If we believe in the guardians of this land?

You do not have to talk about it. You do not have to tell people. You can simply connect when you are out in the woods for a walk. And you can share the experiences if you choose. But we invite you — just you — you who are listening to this story, we invite you to open up to the possibility — if it is something that interests you of course. If it does not then bypass my story and move to the next one.

But, we suspect that if you have been reading or listening thus far, it is because you are interested, and so we invite you. Slow down. Sit. Connect with Nature and open your mind.

And do not expect it to happen the very first time that you do this, because slowing down, sitting, connecting, connecting to Nature, opening your mind to the possibilities, it is like...your scientists would say it would be like strengthening neural pathways. We would say that it is like strengthening that connection: strengthening that connection between the known and the unknown, the seen and the unseen; the magical and the not so magical. The human and the fey.

The more that you strengthen that connection, the more likely you are to experience something magical, something new, something exciting, something unexpected — unexpected in a good way.

And so, we leave this with you now — with these words of encouragement. Sit. Be still. Be quiet. Connect. And keep doing so.

That is all.

# Experience

Open your mind to the possibility of magic: to the Nature spirits and to other dimensions. Pay attention to the times when you're out in Nature and you sense there is someone or something nearby, even if you do not see anything with your eyes.

Be still. Be quiet. Connect when you're out in Nature. Open up to connect with the spirits and the energy of Nature.

Respect Nature in all its territories: the plant realm, the animal realm, and the mineral realm. Pay attention to your attitude as you walk in Nature.

Pay attention to where you tread: the soil, the mosses, the little plants on or alongside the trail. Be conscious of where you place your feet.

*If Trees Could Talk – A Companion Workbook*

# Journal Prompts

## Before the Experience

* Do you believe in the multiverse? Why or why not?

* How do you feel about the possibility of the existence of Nature spirits, such as faeries and other elementals?

* Do you think it's possible that these beings exist, either within our own dimension or outside of it?

* Are you open to the idea of setting the intention to connect with these beings and see what happens? Or would you rather just leave them alone for now, and hope that they do the same?

* Are you open to the possibility of experiencing magic in your life?

* Do you ever sense that there are unseen beings around you when you're in the outdoors?

* How do you feel about that?

* Are you afraid of things that you cannot see, or are you excited about the possibility of getting to know them?

* What's your attitude as you walk in the outdoors?

* Do you ever ask permission to enter a place in Nature, or do you boldly step forward as though you were entitled to be there?

## After the Experience

* How has your attitude changed when you walk in Nature since you began reading this book and doing these activities?

* How often do you pay attention to where you place your feet when you're walking in Nature?

* Do you try to avoid stepping on plants if possible?

* Have you ever found yourself apologizing to some living thing that you've stepped on?

* Have you seen, felt, or experienced any kind of Nature spirit or faerie?

# ALTON PRIORS YEW

**Y**ou are safe here. You are dry here. You are safe from the rain. Safe inside my trunk.

You have seen the sign inside the church. You have seen the official notice — the certification that I am 1,700 years old. And though many people doubt this, it is true. Or at least as true as I know it to be in my interpretation of your human years.

I have stood here for centuries, and centuries, and centuries. And I have seen the changing of the landscape. Though I must say I am pleased that this area has not changed greatly. It is a very quiet village. Twin villages with their twin churches. Things could be worse: things could have changed more.

My trunk is old, old, old, old and it is split in two. This is what allows you to come inside and rest within my trunk.

Twin trunks, like twin churches, twin villages.

And this was a sacred place since far before the Church was here. This was a sacred place always. You can feel the energy here. You can sense the specialness of this place.

This feels harder to you, harder than telling the stories of the other trees you have spoken with. I understand why. Because of my size, because of my great age, it seems as if my story will be more important to tell than the stories of the other trees. And so, this blocks you, this trips you up. It makes it more difficult to tell my story, and yet my story is not more important than the stories of any of the other trees that you have spoken with, and that you will speak with. And that is because, as you know, we are all connected with our network. Our stories are passed down from generation to generation — and so even if I had not survived these 1,700 years, I would have this knowledge. I know that my age is almost impossible for you to grasp: the idea of a tree — one single tree — being alive for that many years. Seventeen centuries...170 decades. This is many, many, lifetimes for you humans.

It is difficult for you to grasp, and yet so many people are drawn here to this Church — to see me. And I am happy to have survived this long. I am happy to thrive. I am happy to have lived this long. I am happy to be an attraction, a focal point, the thing that draws people to this place, to this sacred land. And I wish that more trees could survive to this age, because people respect this age. People respect the years that I have been on this planet...and I can only wish that more people respected other trees in the same way.

I am not valuable simply because I have been on this earth for 1,700 years, I am valuable because I am part of Nature, because I am a tree, like all other trees, like all other plants, like all other shrubs, like all other elements of Nature, we all deserve respect. And as I was saying, I do not deserve more respect. My story is not more important because of my age, because we have this network — and all of the trees that you speak with will have access to these ancient stories because they have been passed down from generation to generation.

You must seek out other old trees, other ancient trees such as myself, and visit them and bring attention to them so that people can visit them; because I sense that, as I have said, people respect age. They respect the longevity of a tree such as myself, and if people can visit ancient trees and have that sense of awe — that sense of respect — sparked in themselves, it will generate — perhaps, perhaps not — but it is my hope that it will generate respect for all the other trees and all the other living beings and all the minerals of this world.

Sometimes it seems that it is a miracle that I am still alive. You look around at the inside of this cave that is my trunk; I have split into two, which they say is normal for a yew of my age.

You are finding this difficult and that is all right. As the very first yew that you spoke with told you, trees have stories, and for us it is important that our stories be told. This is a start. There will be many opportunities to get more stories, to get different stories, to get bigger stories, to get longer stories, to get shorter stories. This is a start.

If you think back to what was going on in this land 1,700 years ago, it will give you an idea of just how long I have been here. All of the things that have happened as I have stood, silently, patiently, quietly, in this churchyard, on this land, even before the church was built. The things I have seen, the people that I have passed. It is a quiet place, there have not been all that many people, but it has been a long, long, time.

People back then had more respect for the land, had more respect for the trees, they had more respect for what Nature has to give. And they did not take without giving back. There was a give and a take. There was not the sense of entitlement that seems to exist today. The sense of: "this land is mine and I can do what I want with it." There was more respect, and I miss that, having seen the changes in attitudes. It is a quiet village. Nothing much has happened here, but I can sense it in the energy, in the thoughts, in the attitudes of the people that walk through here, of the people that visit — that things are different, things are very, very different than they were when I was a sapling, just starting to grow out of the ground here. Things have changed.

And I do believe — we do believe — that things can change; not back to what they were because that can never happen, but they can evolve in a good way. And we can pick up some of what was lost. We can regain some of that respect, that love, that connection with Nature. It is possible. There can be a sort of revival of that connection with Nature, of that respect for Nature, of that belonging with Nature, of that co-existence with Nature. And people can release that sense of entitlement, of dominion, of power, over Nature; because as you have seen, Nature has great power as well. The power of the wind, the power of the rain, the power of streams and rivers, the power of earth, and the power of all living beings.

And sometimes this power of Nature is more than what humanity can handle and sometimes disasters happen. Things can go both ways. But I believe we can reach a place of harmony once more. A place of interaction. A place of working together. A place of harmony. Mutual respect. Connection. Deep connection.

I do not know if I will live to see that day, but I hope that I will. I have lived 1,700 years more or less and perhaps I will live 1,700 more — though I doubt it. That would be quite long for a tree, wouldn't it? But I trust that things will reach that point of harmony.

That is all.

# Experience

Seek out ancient trees and visit them. If you know of a local forest that has particularly large or veteran trees, go to see them. If you do not know of such a place, do some research online and visit them. Tune into the energy of the place where they are located. Bring attention to the trees in whatever way you like: take photos and share them online, blog about your experience, create a video with the tree. Encourage others to visit ancient trees, too.

Cultivate a deep respect for Nature and focus on building a sense of harmony with the natural world; work to regain the respect, the love, and the connection with Nature. Remember to give thanks for the experiences you have.

# Journal Prompts

## Before the Experience

🍂 Do you feel that a being (whether animal, plant, or mineral) is due more respect simply because it's older?

🍂 Or do you believe that all beings deserve the same respect simply because they are alive and are a part of this world?

🍂 Do you believe something else entirely?

🍂 Do you hold the same hope as the Alton Priors Yew does for the future of humanity's relationship with Nature?

🍂 Do you think it's possible for humans to rebuild a new sense of harmony with Nature?

🍂 Do you have hope for the future of our planet?

🍂 How long do you think it might take us to regain a deep sense of respect for and connection with Nature? How many generations will it take?

🍂 Finally, do you know of any ancient trees in your local area that you could visit? If not, have you done the research to find some? When would you like to go see them?

## After the Experience

🍂 Which ancient trees did you visit?

🍂 What were they like?

🍂 How did you feel when you were with them?

🍂 Did you feel more respect for them because of their great age?

🍂 Does spending time in Nature fill you with a sense of harmony?

🍂 Do you feel a greater sense of respect and connection to the natural world since doing these activities?

# WINDMILL HILL HAWTHORN

**Y**ou are correct in saying that this is your place.

This is your home, this is your land, and this is where you belong. And in the same sense that this land is yours, this land is for you, you are for this land...everyone in this world has a land that is for them; where they feel connected, where they feel rooted, where they feel grounded, where they feel right, where it just feels like home. Regardless of whether they go out into Nature and connect with the natural land, some people may sense that one place is right for them, or not. But they can deepen that connection, they can deepen that relationship, they can deepen that deep sense of home by going to Nature around that place and connecting with it: connecting with the trees, connecting with the earth, connecting with the water, the sky, the wind, all of the elements.

Many, many, people have not yet found their abode, their comfortable place, their home, and their spot in the world. And this is sad — because everyone does have a place.

We understand that people make decisions based on the practicalities of life; whether that be finding a job, proximity to family, friends, other things, practical things; but we would suggest that if you have not yet found your home, your place in the world; if you could just travel, visit, go to the places where your heart guides you. Whether that be the next town over, the next country, or halfway around the world, if you feel drawn to a place: visit, experience, connect...and we understand that this sounds just a bit crazy, because again the practical brain comes in and says: I can't afford that, I don't have money for that, what if I want to go to a place that is, as you say, halfway around the world, and I just don't have the money. We would like to suggest, again, that you put aside the practical thoughts, practical ideas, practical solutions, the practical problems and simply allow yourself to dream.

If you have a place in mind, start connecting with it: by reading about this place, you can buy books about the place, you can read online, you can do searches, you can look at photographs, you can look at images, you can collect images, you can make a collage of all your favorite images of this place. And connect with this place on a digital level, on an intellectual level, by reading...and that will start the journey.

There is a reason you are drawn to some places.

And that does not necessarily mean that you have to move halfway around the world and live in this place — but perhaps, these are places that you could visit. And once you make the connection, you may find that it is easier, and easier, for you to visit these places; and it is easier for you to return to these places, and it is easier for you to connect and feel that deep sense of belonging. That sense of "I am home, I am here" that so many people crave.

And so, we would like to remind you, that perhaps this path starts for you by setting aside practical worries, and concerns and simply connect wherever you can by reading online, by reading books — connect, connect, connect. And perhaps you will find the ways, perhaps you will find the practical solutions, on how to get to these places and how to return to these places and how to perhaps one day even live in these places that you are drawn to. But it all starts with that intuitive nudge, that calling of the heart, as it connects to your heartland; to the place where you belong, to the place that feels like home, to the place of your abode, perhaps, perhaps not...but you will be surprised what happens when you answer that call.

And, we feel the need to point out — to recommend, to remind you — how important it is to be still, of the importance of being quiet, of the importance of experiencing. So, when you go to these places — these places that your heart is called to — do not simply rush through them like a tourist, do not book a five-day tour where you are rushing around on buses all day. Do not hike through the land quickly trying to get to your next destination; but simply stop, sit, relax, feel, hear, smell, touch, taste, experience...experience with all your senses.

Turn up the volume of your senses and turn down the speed of your being, the speed of your action taking, the speed of your movements, the speed of your actions.

Slow, slow, slow, slow, slow; and sense, sense, sense, sense, sense. Sense the warmth of the sun on your face. The coolness of the wind on your hands. The sensation of light changing as the clouds move. Smell the freshly cut grass - the good and the bad; smell the sheep dung - for they are here too. Hear the birds, planes, the wind...feel the firmness of a tree against your back. Feel the softness of the grass beneath your hand. Slow, slow, slow and sense, sense, sense.

Become treelike.

This is not the first time that you have heard this advice, but it is good to be reminded. It is always good to be reminded because this rushing around is a habit we see in many people; a habit that can be broken, but it helps to be reminded — in order to break these habits.

This is all.

# Experience

Find your place in the world: travel, visit, experience, connect, dream, read.

Identify the places where your heart guides you to go: start connecting with them, visit them. When you go there: be still, be quiet, and experience the site with all of your senses. Sense, smell, hear, feel the place in every way. Become treelike in that place.

# Journal Prompts

## Before the Experience

- Can you sense when a place is right or wrong for you?
- Have you found your place in the world, your heart place? If so, how did you find it?
- Do you have more than one?
- How does it make you feel?
- Are you living there, or is it a place you visit?
- If you have not yet found your heart place, your place in the world: which places are you drawn to?
- Which places would you like to explore? Where does your heart guide you to visit? Where do you dream of going?
- Which places have you always wanted to visit?
- What parts of the world do you find fascinating?

## After the Experience

- What did you experience when you went to one of these places that you feel drawn to? What was it like? How did you feel? Will you be returning there soon?
- What do you think of this advice to become "treelike"?
- Do you find it easy to slow down and sense the things around you? Or are you constantly moving, taking action, doing things?

# AVEBURY BEECHES

Yes, the wind has died, just a bit, and you can take our story.

We know that there is nothing more beautiful than a tree, though perhaps we are biased. However, the tall brown or gray trunks; the textured bark of our skin; our green leaves which turn colored once a year. We know these things are beautiful and we take pride in being so striking — some of us more than others, but we are beautiful.

And what caught your attention as you were walking towards us were the ribbons tied on our roots, and you have seen the other cluster of trees on the other side, with ribbons tied on the roots and the ribbons tied on the branches. And you have seen that those trees have so many more ribbons than we do. We like the ribbons. We like when people come and place their wishes on us, and they use us as the catalyst for making their wishes come true, for making their dreams come true. We know that we play a role in this. We know that our energy is strong and grounded and powerful, and we know that we can help with this.

And we know that some people come here, and they tie a ribbon on our branches just because they have seen everybody else do it, and perhaps they don't truly believe that we can help make things happen for them. They do not necessarily believe that our energy comes together with theirs to help their dreams become a reality. And yet, if they were to become aware of this, if they were to understand this, if they were to acknowledge this, if they were to consciously ask for help, if they were to consciously harness the power of our energy, which is so deeply grounded, so deeply rooted in this earth...if people were to consciously ask us for help when they place their wishes on our branches in the form of a ribbon, their wishes would be so much more powerful. But they do not know this, and that's why we wanted you to share this story.

We love the ribbons, not because we think they make us more beautiful, because we know that we are perfect, just as we are. We are in Nature: we are strong, we are rooted, and we are grounded. We rise high above the earth.

We know that we are beautiful, and we know that we do not need ribbons to make us more beautiful. It is the wishes that we like — it is the wishes that we want — it is one of the ways that we can help humans. And we love this, we enjoy this, we want to be a part of this. We see this as a kind of play, a kind of way that we can help, a way that we can help people make their dreams come true. But, remember, the more you ask for our help, the more help you will get. The more you become aware of what you are doing when you tie a ribbon onto our branches, the faster your dream will come true, and the more help you will get. Because by asking for our help and by consciously calling in our energy it makes things so much stronger, so much more powerful, because that energy is amplified.

We thank you for coming to talk to us. We thank you for coming to take our story.

We are always here; we are always here to receive: to receive your ribbons, to receive your wishes, to receive your message, to receive your cries for help, your calls for help, we are always here, and we always will be here. Us, our ancestors, us and the trees that come after us, as our ancestors were here before us. We are here to help. We want to help. And we ask you that you please ask us for help.

That is all, thank you.

# Experience

Find a wishing tree in your area, or if you cannot find one, visit a sacred spring or well and see if there is a wishing tree there. If not, ask one of the trees near the spring if you can use it as a wishing tree. Tie a ribbon on the wishing tree or cloutie tree, and consciously harness the power of the tree when you make your wish. Ask the tree for help in making your dream come true. Always remember to give thanks to the trees for their help.

# Journal Prompts

## Before the Experience

- Have you ever seen a wishing tree? If so, have you ever made a wish while tying a ribbon on a branch?
- What types of things have you wished for?
- What types of things could you wish for?
- Did you ever realize that you might elicit the spirit of the tree to help you to make your wish come true?
- Do you think that asking the tree for assistance might help you to make your intentions stronger?

## After the Experience

- How did it feel to consciously ask the tree for help when you made your wish?
- Could you sense the power of the tree's energy?
- Would you like to do this again, either with the same tree or with a different tree?
- What other things could you ask the trees for help with?

# FULBROOK OAK

You are right I am old; I have been here for many, many, years. Hundreds of years in fact. I am not the oldest tree in this field: there are trees older than I, there are trees younger than I, but I am hundreds of years old. And I have seen the passing of time, the passing of time in this quiet, secluded, corner of the world. I have seen the poles put up, for whatever it is that it provides you — electricity, telephone — and the wires that string across this field. I have seen the road put in just on the other side of this fence. I have seen sunsets and sunrises, and I have been here for many, many, many years.

There is a public footpath that goes through this field, and so few people walk down it. It is not a popular trail, this is not a well-traveled trail. And the people who walk it, the people who do walk it, do not stop to connect with us. They may stop to sit underneath the shade of our branches, to have lunch, to have a break, to have a snack. But they do not make contact with us, they do not connect with us, they do not feel us. They do not sense the importance of trees like us, they do not sense our power, they do not sense our age, and they do not sense how long we have been here on this earth. How many generations of humans, how many have walked past us? Because we have been here for a very long time.

People may walk by and think: "oh what big trees, what nice trees," but they do not see us as the grandfathers that we are. We have been here for a long time: we have seen, we have felt.

It is autumn now and our leaves are not yet falling from our branches, but they are about to. Our acorns are starting to fall to the ground. You can hear them as they strike the ground all around you. It is that time of the year again: time for us to go dormant, for us to lie still, for us to shed our leaves, and sleep. And to save our energy for springtime, when it all starts again.

We have seen so many of these cycles, so many of what you call "years": so many, so many, so many. So many springs, so many falls, so many winters, and we flow through the cycles because that's what we do: we have no other option. Not that we would want another option — we just do our thing.

We would, however, wish for some recognition.

Not because we need it, it is not an ego thing, it is a matter of connection, it is a matter of cohabiting — trees and humans — and living together on this planet, on this earth. You see us as you walk on your walks, you see us as you drive down your streets, but there is little connection with us. And the connection with us, the relationship with us, has been lessening over the years. We, the grandfathers, can see this, and we can tell you this. There are fewer people walking, because you have other methods of transportation, and there are fewer people who take time to sit up against our branches, against our trunks, against the logs of our fallen brothers and sisters. Very few people who sit and touch the moss on our trunks, who stop to feel the smoothness, of our acorns, who stop to really connect with us...they are few.

And that is why we would like to encourage you, when you see an old tree, to stop and sit. Sit with your back against our trunk, make yourself comfortable, relax, connect, feel our energy through your back, feel our energy through your spine. Feel our energy. And, if you like, allow it to trickle into your body, to flow into your body, to envelop you.

And feel some of our strength, our strength that goes back for hundreds of years, our strength that has allowed us to grow to this impressive size. We are pretty impressive, I know that. We have massive trunks a broad branch spread, I see my brothers and sisters out here in the field, we are something to be admired but not just admired, we are also something to be appreciated.

I urge you to connect with us, to feel our energy, all you need to do is take a few moments out of your walk and just sit with your back against us. Feel the texture of our trunk, the moss. But most importantly connect with that energy, connect with that life force flow and allow it to flow through you. And see what you experience, see how it feels, give it a try.

Feel it in your heart. Receive.

# Experience

Pay attention to the trees that you pass when you go about your day: whenever you're out walking, or cycling, or driving.

Sit with your back against a tree trunk. Relax, connect, feel their energy through your back and up or down your spine. Allow their energy to flow into your body, and feel their strength. Connect with the life force energy and feel it in your body. Feel it in your heart. Receive. Always remember to give thanks to the trees for their help.

# Journal Prompts

## Before the Experience

* Do you really notice the trees around you when you're out walking, cycling, or driving?

* Do you ever sit or stand with your back against a tree trunk?

* What do you feel when you connect physically with a tree in this way?

* Have you ever noticed any kind of energy flowing from the tree through the back of your heart center?

## After the Experience

* When you went out to consciously connect with the tree, what was it like to connect with its energy?

* How did it feel when you allowed it to flow through you?

* Could you feel it in your heart?

* Were you able to allow yourself to fully receive?

* Is this something that you'd like to repeat, either with the same tree or with other trees?

*If Trees Could Talk – A Companion Workbook*

# PEPER HAROW YEW

This is a big and beautiful estate; there are many old homes here. This church is old. But I have been here much, much, longer — longer than most people think that a tree can be around. I am a yew. We are capable of growing old. You can see that my trunk is almost fully split, and there is an opening in my center, big enough for someone to even climb inside if they wanted to, and you could, and that would be fine. My branches are old, gnarled, missing some leaves on some of them. I have been here since before this church was built, on this sacred site.

There is a sense of peace here, and you can feel it, many feel it. That is why this was considered a sacred site, this was why the church was built here, this is why the estate was built here, this is why people have come to this area. It is like a pocket of calm, and peace, and tranquility and I have presided over this area for many hundreds of years. Perhaps even a thousand...I do not count time the way people do. But I am old, and I have been here to see and to feel the peace in this area over the hundreds of years that I have been here.

I would ask you when you see an old yew like me, whether it is at a churchyard, or somewhere else, to stop, sit, relax, enjoy, feel the calm, feel the peace, soak up the energy. Often us old yews are situated in ancient sacred sites, sites that may have been forgotten or sites that have not been forgotten because the modern church was built. Either way, these places are special. These places are meant for you to come to, to soak up the energy, to feel, to experience. Close your eyes. Relax. Feel the sacred energy of this spot. Do not be bothered about how you feel about the church — this sacred place predates the church. If you disagree with religion, if you dislike it, or however you may feel, sense the energy of this place.

The church bell may be a bit jarring, perhaps unexpected. *(The church bell had just begun to strike the hour, and it was a shock in the otherwise silent afternoon.)*

Close your eyes and allow yourself to soak up this sacred energy. There are benches, spots to sit. Enjoy. And see what you feel, see what you connect with here. See what you can sense here and see what it means to you. I invite you, not just here, but again wherever you see an ancient, giant, yew like me.

That is all.

# Experience

Whenever you see an ancient yew (or other veteran trees that may exist in your region), sit and soak up the energy of the place. Feel the sacred energy of that site. Stop, sit, relax, enjoy the place, feel the peace and calmness of the site. Remember to give thanks to the place for its energy.

# Journal Prompts

## Before the Experience

🌱 Can you sense when you're at a sacred site?

🌱 Why do you think these places were chosen for worship in ancient times?

🌱 What is it about the energy there that you think draws people to these particular sites?

🌱 Do you believe in ley lines, or do you think they're something that was made up to connect the dots of the numerous sacred sites that are scattered all over the world?

## After the Experience

🌱 When you went to visit the ancient tree, were you able to feel the sacred energy of the place?

🌱 Did you feel yourself receiving the energy? What else did you feel?

🌱 Did you sense anything else there? Did it feel like a sacred site?

🌱 Is this something that you'd like to repeat, either in the same place or somewhere new?

# RANMORE MAPLE

You were drawn to me for a reason. Years ago, when you were drawn off the trail, just a bit downhill, to sit against my trunk. There is a special energy here: you can feel it. It is a calm — a sense of peace — as the breeze rustles the leaves of the trees around us, and as it rustles my leaves, too.

Other people are drawn to me, not necessarily for this energy, but because as you have seen there is a geocache nestled amongst the roots of the base of my trunk, hidden by a big white stone. Some people come looking and never find it. Some people find it and then move on. And, occasionally, people will sit and stop and look through the woods at the field that opens up just beyond where we are situated.

I know other trees have encouraged you to sit and spend time, rather than hustling through the woods. I would say the same, but I do not want to dwell on the same topic, so I will add a little detail to it: rest awhile, under a tree. Listen to the birds. Listen to the natural sounds, and to the unnatural sounds — such as an airplane, or the train when it goes by.

Close your eyes. Many people are fearful of closing their eyes in the woods, and we trees do not know why. There are no dangerous animals here, only other humans perhaps. So what I would encourage, when you sit against the base of a tree, is to close your eyes. You, humans, are so, so, dependent on your eyes — on your vision — for sensory input, for information. I would encourage you to open your ears and relax and rest and take in all that you hear: even the sounds that you do not understand — especially the sounds that you do not understand. And I would encourage you to resist the temptation to open your eyes when you hear something, but you are not sure what it is.

Hear the insects as they buzz around you; the leaves rustling in the breeze; the birds in the trees. And note that the longer you sit still, the more sounds you will hear. The squirrels will approach, the birds will approach; all the living things that are mobile in the woods will cease to see you as a threat, and they will come forward.

Rest awhile amongst my roots with your eyes closed...and trust: trust that you are safe, trust that you are protected, trust that all is well. Rest a while with your back against my trunk and soak up the energy and the sounds of the life of the woods. It is autumn now: you can hear an occasional leaf falling, rustling against the floor — the soil of the woods — as it settles.

Enjoy the sounds, enjoy Nature, and enjoy the energy. And again: resist that temptation to open your eyes. You may need to ease yourself into this experience. If you find it exceptionally difficult, you might set yourself a timer: of one minute; three minutes; five minutes; ten minutes; fifteen minutes; half-an-hour. Start with whatever feels like a stretch. And then each time that you go out in the woods you can extend that time; or, perhaps, if you are going out on a long walk, spend one minute against one tree, then walk a while; spend three minutes against another tree, walk some more; five minutes against a third tree...and onwards.

Stretch your comfort zone — stretch your limits — so that you can fully experience the woods, and in particular the sounds of the woods.

That is all.

# Experience

Settle down against a tree and close your eyes and open your ears. Take in all that you hear, and resist the temptation to open your eyes when you hear an unfamiliar sound (obviously, be safe while doing this). If you find this difficult, set a timer for one, three, five, or more minutes. Start with whatever feels like a stretch. Use this workbook to write down your observations once you open your eyes and finish the exercise.

# Journal Prompts

## Before the Experience

* Do you feel safe when you're alone in Nature?
* Do you feel safe enough to sit in silence with your eyes closed?
* Do you think you would be able to keep your eyes closed, even if you heard a sound that you couldn't identify?
* How do you feel about the maple's suggestion of stretching your comfort zone so that you can expand your sense of safety as you fully experience the woods?

## After the Experience

* How did you feel when you closed your eyes in the woods?
* Did any fears come up for you?
* Were you able to keep your eyes closed, even when hearing an unfamiliar sound?
* What was the longest time you were able to keep your eyes closed for?
* How long would you like to try for the next time?
* Most importantly, what did you hear when your eyes were closed that you hadn't noticed when they were open?
* Is this something you'd like to repeat, either in the same place or somewhere new?

# RANMORE OAK

We have had a long relationship. You were first drawn to me the moment you saw me, as you were coming up the hillside, walking through the gate. I am a powerful figure on this hillside; I am one of the oldest trees here, and I am an oak. You may have noticed that we oaks have a certain gravitas. People are drawn to us: they are drawn to our size, our energy, our strength, and our beauty of course.

And you have had some ups and downs here, sitting beneath my branches. You have had a difficult conversation with another person here and that led you to avoid me for some time. And I am here to tell you that trees are the perfect place for difficult conversations, for awkward experiences with other people...or with yourselves.

We are the perfect place to bring troubles and sadness — to bring difficulties, to bring stress — because we can take it on for you; and transmute and change this energy, this uncomfortable, this difficult, this negative energy, if you would call it that. We can help absorb it from you and release it into the ground and transform it into something neutral. And it is important that you know this, and it is important that everyone hearing this story know this; because we can help, we are willing to help, we will help. And if you know that you can do this — we encourage you to take your troubles to the trees and to do so consciously.

Sit on the ground against our trunks, or stand next to us and hug us, or stand up against us with your back to our trunk. You can put your hands — the palms of your hands — on our bark. However you choose to connect with us physically, do so. There is no right or wrong way to do this.

Imagine your worries, your troubles, your sadness, your stress — whatever it is that you have — flowing out of your body and into our trunk. Sense us absorbing that energy and then pulling it down, down, down, down the trunk, down into the roots, into the earth; and transforming that energy into something neutral. It is a process that does not hurt us: it does not hurt the earth, it does not hurt the planet, and it does not hurt anything, because we have this capacity to take what is troubling you and to transform it.

And if you do this consciously, it is all the more powerful. And if you do this on a regular basis, even better for you.

You can pick any kind of tree you want: you can pick a big oak; you can pick a yew; you can pick a holly; you can pick any plant, any tree you want. You could even pick a big shrub, but you might find yourself more drawn to the trees for this task.

To be fair, you could even lie down on the grass and visualize yourself sending this energy into the grass, or to the plants; but, because I am a tree, I would like to suggest that you try this with trees. You could say that I am biased in that I think we are the perfect plant life form to help you in this way.

Feel yourself now, settled in, sitting on the earth, leaning up against my trunk, your hand on the base of my trunk. You can visualize yourself sending that stress, sending that uncomfortableness, sending whatever it is that you want to release out of your body and into my trunk...out of your body and into my trunk. Out of your body and into my trunk, and see it flowing. Flowing like a stream of energy, out of your body and into my trunk. And then from there see it flowing into the earth.

You might want to visualize it coming out of your body a particular color. It could be red, or it could be something else: brown, black or white, whatever works for you. And then, perhaps, as you see that energy flowing out of your body and into my trunk and down my trunk, down into my roots, down into the earth, you may want to visualize that energy changing color as it flows.

If you sense a darker color coming out of your body you may sense it turning lighter, and lighter and lighter and lighter. And as it flows away into the earth, you may sense it turning into a bright, white light of energy, disbursing into the earth beneath you, into the earth all around you and spreading out as this neutral energy that has been transformed and transmuted and changed by the power of Nature, by the power of the trees; and by the power of you being willing to do this work. So this is what I ask you: bring your troubles to the trees. We will take care of them for you.

Thank you, thank you, thank you.

This is all.

# Experience

Take your troubles, sadness, difficulties, and stresses to a tree. Sit on the ground against a tree, or stand next to it and hug it, or stand up with your back against the trunk. Imagine your worries and stress flowing out of your body and into the tree. Sense the tree absorbing the energy and carrying it down into the roots and into the earth, where it is transformed into neutral energy. Do this on a regular basis, whenever you're feeling unhappy or unwell. Remember to give thanks to the tree for its help.

See **http://hollyworton.com/trees** for a guided meditation you can download, which will help you with this.

# Journal Prompts

## Before the Experience

* Have you ever had a difficult conversation with someone when you were out in Nature, perhaps while sitting underneath a tree?

* Were you aware that the trees might be able to help you through your troubled times?

* How do you feel about the idea of taking your worries to the trees?

* Do you have a particular tree in mind that you'd like to ask for help with this?

## After the Experience

* When you took your troubles to a tree, what issues did you bring to it?

* How did you feel when you were doing this activity?

* Was it easy for you to visualize sending your troubles to the tree to be absorbed?

* How did you feel afterward?

* Is this something you would like to try again, either with the same tree or with a different one?

# GRANDFATHER TREE

**W**elcome back.

I know that I am one of the first trees that you made a connection with. I know I am the first tree that you specifically searched for and sought out a connection with.

I sent you that message because I knew that you needed the challenge of finding me — the Grandfather Tree — amongst all the other trees that you have passed on your walks. And you knew instantly which tree I was, but you still questioned yourself. You still questioned yourself, and you asked other trees if they were the Grandfather Tree, while at the same time, a part of you knew that it was me. And you have come back many times in the different seasons and you are here now connecting, learning, receiving.

I am here to tell you, and your readers, to trust. Trust, trust, trust yourself. One of the most important things that you can cultivate, in the inner garden of your mind, is a deep, deep, deep trust of yourself. And the reason why this is my message for you is precisely because you did not trust yourself when I sent the message that you were to find me — first you received the message not directly, but through someone else, and then you questioned who I was.

So, I am here to remind you — all of you — to trust yourselves.

It can be hard for people to trust themselves in this day: there are so many distractions, so many worries, so many stresses, and so much information. There are so many signals that you are receiving that it can be very, very hard to lower your antennae and to tune in to your inner self, your inner knowing, your inner knowledge, your inner wisdom. Tune into your own signals, your private signals, which circulate within yourself, within your body, within your mind, within your system.

Trust yourself.

There are many ways to do this. But the most important — the easiest — way, is to allow yourself to slow down, to give yourself permission to slow down. In general, in life — and also as you walk in the woods — allow yourself to take slower steps to walk at a more leisurely gait. Slow, slow, slow. And then sit: sit on a log; sit with your back against a tree; sit on a grassy field, sit wherever you want. Sit, and this does not even have to do with Nature: it can be done at your home, it can be done at your office; it can be done in a park; it can be done anywhere.

Sit in silence. You do not have to meditate, but you can. Just feel yourself slowing down, feel your thoughts slowing down, allow all the muscles of your body to relax, and especially your face: these can often be the last muscles that you allow to relax. Feel yourself relax...and go within, whatever that means for you.

Slow down.

And allow any messages to come to light: messages from your inner self, messages that you need to hear. Allow yourself to spend time with yourself on a regular basis...slowing down...slowing down...slowing down. And allow yourself to receive from yourself. And slowly you will learn to look inward for advice, to look inward for wisdom, to look inward for a sense of direction.

Trust yourself. This is the biggest gift you can give yourself. And for your readers this is something that I would like to give you as a challenge: I call myself Grandfather Tree. I would like to challenge you to go out and find your grandfather tree. It could be a tree that you have already seen on one of your walks; it could be a new tree that you have yet to discover. Set the intention to find this tree and make contact with it and trust yourself that you have found the right tree, the correct tree, your grandfather tree.

This is all.

# Experience

Sit in silence or meditate: slow down and listen to your inner guidance. Feel your body slow down as you tune into your own inner signals. Go within. Trust yourself. Remember, this is the biggest gift you can give yourself.

Try the mind decluttering meditation to clear your mind of thoughts and open up to hear your inner voice.

Find your own Grandfather Tree and make contact with it. Trust that you have found the right tree.

# Journal Prompts

## Before the Experience

* Do you fully trust yourself? On a scale of 1 to 10, with 10 being highest, how much do you trust yourself?

* Do you trust the decisions you make, or do you constantly second guess yourself?

* Do you believe that it's safe for you to trust yourself?

## After the Experience

* When you did this exercise of slowing down and listening to your inner guidance, what was it like to slow down and open up to your inner wisdom?

* How did it feel?

* Did you receive any guidance or messages?

* Did you come to any new awareness?

* Were you able to trust these messages?

* Did you find your own Grandfather Tree?

* Was it a tree you were already aware of, or is it a new one you met while doing this activity?

* Did you trust that you found the right one, or did you question yourself?

* Did you try the mind decluttering meditation? How many times did you try it? Did it help you to get things out of your head and into a system for getting them done?

* Do you feel different now that you've cleared your head? Is it easier to hear the voice of your intuition?

* Do you think you'll continue using the mind decluttering meditation to keep your head clear of unnecessary information?

# THE GRANDMOTHERS

You are correct, we are the grandmothers.

You were surprised when you returned to us to see that we are not very old trees. But we hold the energy, and the connection, and the information, and the tales of the trees that have come before us in this grove, on this land.

You have been coming here for many years, and you can sense that this is a special place...and you are right. The energy here is special, it is different. And it draws not just you but other people, as you can see by the graffiti on our bark. You see the ring of stones where people will light fires at night. You see the litter, which you occasionally come to pick up. You see the abandoned tent poles. This place has long drawn all kinds of people: people with good intentions, who have respected us, and people who have used this place as a secluded site to drink. You can even see an empty carton of beer over there.

People come and go. We are glad to be visited. We are not glad to have people spray paint things on our trunks, on our bark. But we are glad to provide a place where people can soak in this energy, even if they do not understand what it is or why they come here.

This is a quiet place, with the exception of the train that goes by, off in the distance. Whenever you feel a place like this, sit and soak up the energy even if you do not understand **why** it is that you believe it to be a special place. You do not need to understand the specifics. The fact that you sense the specialness of the energy is enough for you to know. And if you feel drawn to return to places like this, come back: as often as you can, as often as you want to, as often you choose to. Come and visit these special places in the woods.

As you know, our story was not complete the last time, and as you know you are here to collect a story of personal power. The words that we gave you on your last visit were simply an introduction to the things we have to say to you. You were not ready to receive the full story the last time you were here, and that is why it was so difficult for you. It is why you had to return. We are glad that you have returned and that it is now time to transmit the message that we have for you. Personal power has long been an issue for you — and for many, many, other people — and this is something that we can help with.

We are trees. We are tall, and we are deeply rooted in the ground. Not all of us, of course: you see the young yew tree straight in front of you, some of her roots coming out of the ground, leaning to the side. We are not all so fortunate to have deep, deep, roots, but most of us do. We are standing tall, we are standing grounded, and we are standing strong.

*If Trees Could Talk – A Companion Workbook*

When you think about personal power and what it means to you, we suggest that you think of the trees. Think of us Grandmothers, or of any other trees you have seen on your walks: in parks, anywhere. You know what a tree looks like, you can easily visualize one. And so we would recommend that you stand wherever you are, and you close your eyes. Feel roots coming out of your feet, going down into the earth. Down, down, down, connecting with the power and the energy of the planet Earth.

Sense yourself becoming a tree. You might want to stretch your arms up to the sky, as you envision branches growing out of them, branching off into smaller ones, leaves sprouting on them. As you grow and flourish into a deeply rooted tree, strong, and grounded, and beautiful with your foliage, really **feel** what that feels like. Feel what it feels like to be a tree, just being **you**. Pick whatever type of tree you want: you can be a holly, you can be an oak, you can be a yew, you can be a beech, you can be a sycamore, an elder. You can be whatever tree comes naturally to you, whatever tree you feel most drawn to.

And **feel**! Feel that sense of being strong and tall. And you might want to speed up time so that you can grow and feel the girth of your trunk expanding, as new layers of bark grow on your trunk, and new rings form within you. And you grow stronger and stronger and more solid.

Really sink into that feeling and **experience** it. Stay here for as long as you need to, experiencing the sense of treeness, of **being** the tree, of **feeling** the tree, of feeling the **strength** of the tree, the **power** of the tree, the **energy** of the tree. Really feel what that feels like, and when you are ready to come back to the present moment, bring that sense of treeness with you, and this will help you tap into your own personal power.

You can do that visualization as often as you like, as often as you need to, as often as you feel the need to, as often as you want to.

Personal power is a **feeling** — like that feeling of treeness — and it is multi-layered. It is not something that most people will achieve overnight, or after one simple visualization. It is made up of the layers of self-trust, self-love, self-acceptance, self-esteem, self-confidence, self-value, self-worth. And it is the sense of all of these things being deeply grounded and connected with all the multiple layers of your being: your conscious mind, your subconscious mind, your superconscious mind. It is your regular everyday self, connected with your Higher Self, or soul, or whatever it is that you personally choose to call it.

The more you can do to connect with **all** these parts of you and to activate and amplify self-love and self-acceptance and self-trust, all of that work, this multi-layered, multi-dimensional work, will help contribute to your own sense of personal power. You can do this work in whatever way is natural to you. You can do your beliefs work and your energy work: you have so many different techniques and modalities and ways of working with this. You can do visualizations, like the tree visualization that I just shared with you.

If you are feeling powerless in your life, know that many, many, people feel the same: this is quite normal, do not chide yourself for this, do not feel bad about yourself for this, do not feel like there is something wrong with yourself for this. Many, many, people — I would say most people, **we** would say most people — feel powerless, or very nearly powerless in their lives, in their everyday lives. At the very least, they do not feel grounded and strong in their power. And yes, that is another thing that we are: we are strong — even that yew tree that is bending over, as her roots are coming up from the ground on one side. She is strong, her wood is strong.

When you fully step into your personal power, you will **feel** strong. Now, we recognize that some people may have fears — fears about power. Power can be such a dirty word, and some people have such a bad concept of power. Power is neither good nor bad: it is neutral, you can choose to step into your power and use it for good, or you can choose to step into your power and use it for not-good.

When we share these messages with you, we are sharing them with the intention that you will step into your personal power and use it for good, because there are so many good things that can be done. And there are so many good things that are not done, that are not happening because people are not choosing to step into their power. They are choosing to be victims. They are choosing to **feel** small, they are choosing to **play** small, they are choosing to be invisible.

Because power is scary sometimes. Sometimes it doesn't feel safe. It is unknown, maybe outside your comfort zone, maybe new to you. That's why we are here, we The Grandmothers: we are here in our grove to share with you these messages of personal power. And there are certain places in the woods, as we mentioned in the first part of our message here, where you might feel drawn to. And if you do go to these places, know that the trees can help you with your personal power; because we are strong, and we can help transmit that energy to you.

We recognize that this is a big ask, we recognize that this sounds like a big task. And we would like you to **choose** power. You will know if this feels right for you, if now is the time. And even if it is not the time now, but you sense that it might be the time in the future to choose power, put your hand on your heart and say in your own words:

*I choose power for the good. I choose to step into my personal power. I am ready, willing, and able to step into my personal power and to live a life where I am grounded in my personal power, which I choose to use for the good.*

Make that statement to yourself, to the universe, to the trees, to your world. And start doing the work: start doing the work to call back your power, to **feel** your power, to understand that power can be used for many, many, many beautiful things. Power can be good. It is neutral, and it is **how** you choose to use it that matters. And the more people that choose to step out of powerlessness and hopelessness and victimhood, and step away from those things and into their personal power, the better. The more people that choose the path of personal power for good, the faster this world will transform, and the more people that use their personal power for good, the more this good will be amplified, and that energy will crowd out the people who are currently choosing to use their power for not-good.

So we encourage you to make your statement, to take your stand — even if you feel you are not ready. This may not feel comfortable to you. It may feel too big for you. We encourage you to do so anyway. Start by calling this to you. Do not be afraid: it will not happen all at once. It will be like everything else in your life: step by step, you will grow, you will change, you will transform, and you will feel strong and grounded in yourself — in your true self, as you amplify that personal power and that state of self-love, self-acceptance, self-worth, self-trust, that you have within you. It is already there, you do not need to go outside yourself to look for it, you simply need to tap into what you already have. And if you feel that you don't have any of those things — maybe some of them, but most of them not — know that there is a **seed** of all those things within you, so no matter how bad you may feel about yourself today, no matter how bad you may feel about your life or your experience, you have the seeds within you. You have the seeds of self-love, the seeds of self-worth,

*If Trees Could Talk – A Companion Workbook*

the seeds of self-acceptance, the seeds of self-trust, the seeds of everything you need to fully step into your personal power and live a life of power for good.

We are so glad that you have returned to receive this message because it is so, so, so, important for as many people as possible to hear this message and know that however you may feel right now, this is possible for you. It is possible for you today to choose power for good.

That is all.

# Experience

Perform the tree visualization (see **http://hollyworton.com/trees** for a guided meditation you can download, which will help you with this).

Work on your sense of self-trust, self-love, self-acceptance, self-esteem, self-confidence, self-value, and self-worth. Do what you can to improve these areas of your life.

Choose power.

Declare: "I choose power for the good. I choose to step into my personal power. I am ready, willing, and able to step into my personal power and to live a life where I am grounded in my personal power, which I choose to use for the good."

# Journal Prompts

## Before the Experience

🌱 How do you feel about the concept of personal power? Do you think power is good or bad?

🌱 Do you feel powerful or powerless in your life?

🌱 Have you ever felt like you were a victim of your circumstances?

🌱 Have you ever felt that bad things just happened to you, and that you were powerless to do anything about them?

🌱 How do you think it might feel to flip all this on its head and step into your own power?

🌱 How do you feel about taking the oath of The Grandmothers?

## After the Experience

🌱 How did you feel when you said the declaration?

🌱 What was it like to choose power?

🌱 How powerful did you feel before making the declaration, and how did you feel afterward? Was there a shift?

🌱 What else can you do to fully step into your personal power?

🌱 How else can you choose power in your life?

🌱 What can you do to cultivate your sense of self-trust, self-love, self-acceptance, self-esteem, self-confidence, self-value, and self-worth?

🌱 If you choose not to take the oath of The Grandmothers — why is this? Are you afraid of something? Why do you think it doesn't feel right to you? Do you think that you might do it in the future?

🌱 If you did the tree visualization, what was it like? How did it feel?

🌱 What type of tree did you choose to be, and why?

🌱 What was it like to feel the strength, the power, and the energy of yourself as a tree?

*If Trees Could Talk – A Companion Workbook*

# THE THREE WITCHES

**W**e are The Three Witches. We are here in this wood that you have always found special, that you know is special, that you know has a different energy. And the energy that is here comes from the land. And it also comes from the trees, because we have chosen to grow here, and we have soaked up the energy of this land, in this particular spot.

We are The Three Witches. We call ourselves that because we are here to teach witchy stuff.

It is not a coincidence that we had never caught your attention before. And now so close to the day of Samhain is when your eye was drawn to us — the second you stepped into this wood, in fact. We call ourselves The Three Witches not because we are here to help with witchcraft, or to teach you spells. We are not here to tell you a story of magic, at least not magic in the sense that you may be thinking. It is a different kind of witchy stuff that we are here to talk about.

You have become interested lately in the stories of ancient priestess-hood, of ancient feminine spiritual empowerment, and this is the energy that we embody, the three of us. We are here to tell a tale that will hopefully help any women reading this story to step into their soft power, or to at least take a step towards their soft power. And to any men who may be reading this, we encourage you to welcome the women in your lives as they step into this soft power, and we encourage you to step into it yourselves.

It is different, it is new, it will feel new, but it does not have to be scary, because not all that is new is scary. Not all that is new is meant to be feared. And any of you reading this that have any other gender, no matter what you identify yourself as; know that this is the way of the future. Listen up.

The old ways are coming back in a new way.

We know that sounds a bit like a riddle. It sounds like: what does that mean? But, the old ways of women fully stepping into their power in a soft, feminine, way, in a grounded way, in a witchy way, is coming back but in a modern form. This is Divine feminine power, this is power meant to heal, to help, to make a positive difference in the world. This is light power, and we do not mean light in the sense of "not strong": we mean it in the sense of white light — of bright, luminous power. This is what we mean.

And we encourage you to open your mind to what this might look like, to what this might feel like. And this is something that the trees can help with: if you are ever out walking on a trail, walking in the woods, walking in a park and you sense a tree with witchy energy, witchy power, witchiness, approach it. You will know when you feel it. Go up to that tree and connect however you choose. You can sit against the trunk. You can sit and touch the bark. You can stand and do whatever you like. You can make contact with that tree and ask the tree to help you connect with your own Divine feminine power.

And if you do not identify as a woman, ask that tree to help you see this power in women, to help the women in your life step into this power. And if you do not identify as a woman, ask that tree to help you step into your own Divine feminine power, because everyone can have both Divine feminine power and Divine masculine power within themselves. This is the way of the future, this is the natural flow of events, this is the natural course of change. It has been long in coming and it is starting to happen. The time is now, and we encourage you all to embrace this. This is not women stepping into the strong, masculine, power. This is not that. This is not what you may think of power — it is very soft and grounded and flowy. It is very different. It will feel new, it will seem new, but it is old, old, old, and yet it is new in a way — it has evolved since the old days.

And we are here, we The Three Witches, to remind you of this. We are here to remind you. We are here to encourage you to step into this energy, for it is delicious. It is the energy of the magical old crone, it is the energy of the magical maiden, it is the energy of the magical mother. It is the energy of that soft, beautiful, Divine, feminine power.

And if you have not yet experienced it, then perhaps you have seen it in someone else. Perhaps you have seen it in some woman that you find to be magnetic for some reason or another. That is the energy that we speak of. It is lovely, is it not? We do enjoy this energy, and we do enjoy seeing women stepping into this energy. The more women who embrace this soft, feminine, power, the more women who will be helping to bring life to the world. This is beauty. This is love energy. This is Divine. We will say it once more: it is delicious energy and we hope that you enjoy your journey as you discover it and perhaps step into it.

Thank you for coming to us, thank you for seeing us today, thank you for collecting our story, and thank you for beginning to step into your own Divine feminine power. We welcome you on this journey; we are delighted that you have read our story.

Thank you, thank you, thank you. This is all for today.

# Experience

Open your mind to what Divine feminine power might look like or feel like, and ask a tree to help you step into it. Remember to give thanks to the tree for its help.

# Journal Prompts

## Before the Experience

✸ How do you feel about this concept of Divine feminine power?

✸ Is it something that you resonate with?

✸ Is it something that you're willing to accept into your life?

✸ Are you willing to tap into this energy, and to help others in your life cultivate this?

✸ If you don't like the terms "feminine" and "masculine" energy, what words do you prefer?

✸ What do you think Divine feminine power might look like? Feel like?

✸ Do you believe in the power that you have as an individual to help change the world?

✸ If not, what would you need to believe in order to truly feel the power you have inside you to change things, even on a small scale?

## After the Experience

✸ How did you feel when you asked the tree to help you to step into your Divine feminine power?

✸ The Three Witches said that it was delicious energy: were you able to sense that? How else would you describe it?

✸ How has your life changed since you asked for this help?

# SACRED SPRINGS SYCAMORE

It is very important that you allowed yourself some time to slow down before recording my story. It is important that you allowed yourself to sit against my trunk and soak up some of the energy of the place, for this is a special place, and you know it. You can feel it as soon as you come over the little fence and cross the river. Even when the river is dry, you feel a sense of crossing into another realm — which you are not exactly doing, but you **are** crossing into a very special place: a place of the elementals. And you know this because it was told to you, but you would have sensed that energy anyway, even if you had come without knowing. When you have brought friends here, they have sensed it. All the people that come here feel something special, even if they don't understand it. But very few people walk up to this little hill, into this little wood, where we are, where I am situated.

From here you have a view of the fields beyond, of the hill, the sun in the sky. You are surrounded by green, and you have the spring down below — that is where the center of the energy is, with the willow tree down below — and I suspect that tree will have a story for you, too. What I am here to tell you is to pay attention to these spots, to allow yourself to return as many times as you feel drawn to.

But I encourage you to spend time here. Not just five minutes, ten minutes: come, look around, leave. You can sit, you can have a cup of tea from your flask, you can have lunch, and you can sit and close your eyes and soak up the energy of this place and open yourself up to connect with the other beings that reside here. Just because you cannot see them, does not mean that they are not here. Some people can see them, as you know, but whether you can or you can't, it does not matter. You may want to ask permission to come into their special place, you might want to ask permission to stay awhile. Do whatever feels right for you. But you know that they are here, and know that they are not to be feared, no matter what stories you may have heard about them.

Stay awhile and close your eyes and open yourself up to the magic of this land. Soak up the energy. Sit, get comfortable, lie down, but stay awhile. If it is cold, you might want to put on an extra layer of clothing, as your temperature can drop. But stay awhile. Stay awhile and open yourself up to the possibilities of places like this, of connecting with the elementals, of connecting with the Nature spirits. Of connecting with the plant spirits, the tree spirits, the green spirits, the Green Man, the Green Lady, Mother Nature, earth. It is especially easy to access these energies in a place like this, and it is particularly easy at this time of the year. If you are seeking to have a deeper connection with these types of spirits and energies, now would be a good time to come, now, or in May — or any time of the year, there is no bad time to come — to make a connection, to express your interest in communicating with them and developing a relationship with them, and to help them by caring for the land.

There are things that everyone can do. The first that comes to mind is recycling, but that is the norm now. That has been the norm for years and years, but think about how you can conserve energy — resources — this is how you help the planet, this is how you help Nature, by leaving a lighter footprint, by being more respectful if you are drawn to Nature. If you are drawn to the earth, if you are drawn to walking, to being outdoors, why would you not want to care for the planet, to care for the earth, to love it, to respect it? You may find that the more time you spend outdoors, the more than you will want to do: to care for the planet and care for the gifts that Mother Earth gives us. For she is here — she is everywhere, but her spirit is especially strong here.

So, I encourage you to come, come to places like this. Return as often as you feel drawn to. And I encourage you to change your life and change your habits. Change your way of thinking, change your actions, so we can care for this land, this land that gives you so much.

That is all. Thank you.

# Experience

Go to places of special energy and open yourself up to the magic of the land: to the possibility of connecting with the elementals and the Nature spirits. Remember to give thanks to the place for the experience, and for whatever else you may receive.

Help them and help Nature by caring for the land: recycling, conserving energy, leaving a lighter footprint. Change your life and your habits to help care for the Earth.

# Journal Prompts

## Before the Experience

* What more can you do to care for the land and our Earth? You probably already recycle at home, so what else could you do?

* How else can you be more respectful to Nature?

* How can you change your life to show more respect for our Earth?

* What habits can you change?

* What things can you do differently?

* What actions can you take — big or small — to help the planet?

* Are there any sacred springs in your area? If you're not aware of any, look for them online and identify where some might be.

* Do you believe in elementals and Nature spirits?

* Are you open to the possibility of believing in them?

* Do you sense when certain places have a magical feel to them?

* Why do you think this is? What do you think is going on there?

## After the Experience

* Where did you go that was a place of special energy? Did you find a sacred spring?

* Did you feel the presence of any Nature spirits while you were there?

* Did the place have a magical feel to it?

* What actions have you taken to better care for our Earth?

* What more could you do to help our planet?

*If Trees Could Talk – A Companion Workbook*

# WHITE ROAD OAK

The reason I told you to get on with it earlier is because you need to get over yourself when it comes to receiving these stories. Who cares what people think? As you can see, people don't care, people just barely look at us. You have just watched a group of about twenty people who have clearly come to this forest to see the ancient trees that live here, and they walked by, paused for a moment, and continued on. The guide did not encourage them to connect with me, to touch me, to spend some time in my presence, to feel my energy, nothing. It was just: "oh look at that tree, this is a big oak," and then they moved on. And they will do the same with all of the other trees they visit: today, tomorrow, and quite possibly always.

It is fine to come and look at trees. Obviously, we are not offended by this. It is better than nothing: it is better than **not** coming to look at trees. But we urge you to **connect** more with the trees. We are ancient, and I am hundreds of years old. I have been here for years and years and years, for generations of you humans.

Please stop a while underneath our branches. Stop, rest, feel, experience. There are many people here who do not even stray from their path to come and look at me. You have just seen a dog walker pass by, glance over her shoulder because she saw you, and she must have seen me. I am much bigger than you are! But did she divert from her track, her path, to come and look at me? No, because she is just walking her dogs.

And this is fine, this is okay. We trees are pleased any time anyone comes to walk amongst us, whether it is to walk your dogs, or for a morning run, or for whatever. This is all fine and good.

But, if you are the kind of person who wishes to deepen your relationship with Nature, and who wishes to deepen your relationship with the trees, and the plants and all of the green things, then we urge you to slow down. Don't walk so fast; don't move so fast, just **slow down**. And spend more time, walk more slowly, linger longer, and experience with all your senses: your sight, your smell. Do you even **smell** the forest? Pick up the leaves now that it is autumn, pick up the leaves from the forest floor, and smell them. Smell an old rotted log. Smell the green fluffy moss. Smell the trunk of a tree. Smell the air.

When you go to the woods, are you really experiencing it with all your senses? This is another way that you can better connect with the woods, with Nature, with the green things. And we encourage you to do this. There are so many delicious smells. The soil: just kneel down and press your nose to the earth and smell — you might feel silly doing it, but that's okay, no one will care. They might look at you funny, but who cares?

And for those of you who have children: we would encourage you — I would encourage you — to see if your children would play in this way: to smell the forest, to touch the forest, to connect in different ways with their senses. It is wonderful to see children walking in the woods, but if you can encourage them to connect with us at a **deeper** level, that is even better. Children are the future of this world, and the more connected they are to Nature the better it will be for this Earth, the better for this planet, the better for you, the better for me, the better for everyone who lives here. So bring them outdoors, bring them out dog walking, bring them walking, bring them in the woods, and if you can encourage them to connect at a deeper level, encourage them to touch, feel, smell — even taste if you are out when there are berries that are edible. Teach them to forage, and learn to forage yourself.

Connect, connect, connect at a deeper level, and encourage your children to do the same. Encourage your nephews, your nieces, your grandchildren. You may be surprised to see how willing some children are to make these deeper connections, and you can make it play, you can turn it into play: you can make a checklist of different kinds of trees to find. Different kinds of things to smell, things to touch, things to feel, things to experience.

And ask them how they feel as they connect with each tree: ask them if each tree feels differently, or if they feel the same, or what they feel or how they feel. Ask them if they can sense the personality of the tree. They might think you are silly, or they might not, you never know. Make a game with it. Take your children out into the woods and see if you can turn this deeper connection into play. This is very important for the future. And we encourage you to have fun with it. If you do not have children in your life, we would encourage you to play yourself, to play with your senses in the woods. Slow down and have fun.

That is all.

# Experience

Slow down and experience the forest with all your senses: smell the leaves, the rotting logs, the moss, the tree trunks, the air, the earth. Play with your senses in the woods.

Bring the children (and other adults!) in your life to smell the forest, touch the forest, and connect with the forest using their senses. Learn how to forage, and teach them to do it, especially when the berries are ripe. Ask them how they feel as they connect with each tree: ask them if each tree feels different, how it feels. Make a game of it (even with the adults!).

# Journal Prompts

## Before the Experience

* Do you ever take the time to focus on the smells of the forest?

* Do you ever pick up some damp fallen leaves or a tuft of moss to smell them? Have you ever bent down to smell a rotting stump?

* What can you do to encourage other people in your life — especially children — to connect more deeply with Nature?

* If you made an effort to slow down, what did you experience?

* What smells did you discover?

* What are your dominant senses?

* What senses do you use less often when you're in the outdoors? How can you use them more often?

## After the Experience

* If you invited someone else out to experience Nature, what was it like to take children (or other adults) out into the woods?

* Did you make a game of connecting with the trees? What did they think?

* How did you feel when you were playing with them?

* What other things could you do to help the children (and other adults) in your life connect with Nature?

* What other people in your life could you invite to share this experience with you?

# SAVERNAKE BEECH

Thank you for taking the time to stop.

My message for you is to encourage you to return to the same places throughout the seasons. If you find a special place that you like, such as this — which I know that you didn't like so much the first time you came, and perhaps you are not liking so much this time, but you are drawn here — then return to it. You were here in spring and you are now here in the fall — and it is a very different experience.

You recognized me as soon as you saw me, but as you walked up to my trunk you saw the fungus flourishing at the base of my roots. You did not see this the last time in the spring because it was not that time of the year for the fungus to come up — **now** is the time.

You can see that my leaves are different: most of them are still green on the branches, and there is also a beautiful reddish yellow carpet of fallen crunchy leaves at my base. And I would like to encourage you to visit the same sites at different times of the year because you will see different things, you will smell different things, you will feel different things, you will experience different things. And by seeing different things in the same places, in every season of the year, this will help you to connect with the cycle of the year, the wheel of the year, the turn of the seasons. Now, of course, you know that autumn is when the leaves fall, winter is when it is cold, spring is when the flowers come, summer is when it is warm, but it is so much more than that. There is so much more detail, there is so much more to experience in each season of the year, in each month of the year, everything is so different.

You can see the holly straight in front of you, she has got berries on her branches, and she did not have berries when you came here in the spring. The smells were different, the air was different. The air is so crisp and chill today that you have to wear gloves. You did not need gloves when you were here in the spring; that was a different experience. And so I encourage you to find these special places and visit them over and over, at least once in each season. And perhaps to write about your experiences: you can get a notebook and save a few pages for each spot, for each site. You see that robin on the holly branch — what other birds do you see? What sounds do you hear? What smells do you smell? What textures do you touch? What do you see? What is different about all the trees and the shrubs and plants? Are there fruits out? Are there flowers out?

Dedicate several pages to each site and each time you go, write down as much as you can about what you see and smell and experience. Because this is part of deepening your connection with Nature: it is returning to the same sites and observing and experiencing and feeling. How do you feel? You, for example, feel cold. The air has a crispness about it that makes it such a delicious time to visit the woods. The sky is blue and clear, and it is a perfect, perfect day to be outdoors. And as you sit, under my branches, an occasional leaf will fall on you, and this is part of the connecting.

So, what I have for you is the task of recording your experiences in particular places as you visit them throughout the year. You might use small notebooks and have a separate notebook for each place. Do whatever feels right for you.

And if it feels like too much work, then just pick one place and set the intention: put it in your calendar and see if you can make it happen. Take it out to the same place over and over again — at least four times a year in the different seasons. See what you see, see what you smell, see what you feel, see what you hear, but linger. See if you can connect with one particular tree throughout the four seasons, see how that tree looks and smells and feels. See if that tree's energy shifts throughout the year. And just linger.

Spend your time and perhaps observe other people as well. Observe how they experience the spot throughout the different seasons: do they walk faster in the winter, do they linger less? Are they in a hurry just to get their dog walked and get back to the car? Observe how other people experience Nature in different seasons. Experience how **you** experience Nature in the different seasons: how do you feel? Are you cold, did you not wear enough layers? Do you prefer one season to the other? Which is your favorite season? What is your order of preference for all four seasons? But linger. Linger.

Do you hear the delicious rustling of leaves in the wind? I love that sound. You would not have heard that a minute ago or a few minutes ago before the breeze picked up. I love that sound because I can hear my leaves rustle and I can hear the leaves of other trees rustling as well, and I feel like it is a song that we create: a symphony, of rustling leaves in the breeze.

And so this is my task for you: return, return, return to the same site or same sites, throughout the seasons. And experience, and record your experiences, because you may forget.

I hope that you enjoy the symphony of the trees when the wind blows. I thank you. This is all.

# Experience

Visit the same site at different times of the year. What do you see, smell, feel, hear? Feel the energy of the place with your body, and also touch the textures of the tree bark, the leaves, and the earth. Are there any fruits, flowers, fungi? What animals are around?

See if you can connect with one particular tree throughout the four seasons; see how that tree looks and smells and feels. See if that tree's energy shifts throughout the year.

Observe other people at this site and see how they experience the location throughout the different seasons: do they walk faster in the winter, and do they linger less?

Use this workbook or get a journal or notebook and dedicate several pages to each place, writing down as much as you can each time you go. Visit this site at least four times a year, one for each of the seasons, or turn it into a special pilgrimage that aligns with the wheel of the year: the solstices and equinoxes, and the midseason holidays on February 1, May 1, August 1, and October Put this in your calendar to make sure you remember to do it, since this is an ongoing activity.

# Journal Prompts

## Before the Experience

- Are there certain places in Nature that you naturally tend to visit many times throughout the year?
- Have you ever stopped to record your experiences, or to compare what it's like in the different seasons?
- How do you think it might deepen your connection to those places if you were to journal about what each experience is like?
- If you were to pick just one place to record your experiences and observations throughout the seasons, where would you go?

## After the Experience

- What was it like to visit the same site throughout the year?
- Where did you go?
- What did you experience?
- What did you learn?
- How did you experience Nature in the different seasons: how did you feel?
- Do you prefer one season to the other? Which is your favorite season?
- What is your order of preference for all four seasons?
- Did you visit your site on the pagan festivals, or at random times throughout the year?
- If you went there on the pagan festivals, did you sense anything different on those dates?
- Is this something that you would like to repeat next year, whether in the same place or in a different location?

*If Trees Could Talk – A Companion Workbook*

SAVERNAKE BEECH | 131

# POINTING OAK

**M**y name is Pointing Oak. You heard my message before you even saw me or knew that I was here. You were looking for a different tree — a pair of trees. And instead, you came across me first, and you heard me before you saw me, because this is such an important message.

As you were coming around the trail, making a right turn, you stepped on an old empty bottle, and it crunched loudly under your feet. You were surprised, you looked down, and you kept going. And then you realized what you had done, and you turned and went back and picked up the bottle, and this is what I would like people to know: you always carry a rubbish bag in your backpack and yet you do not always use it.

I would like to encourage all of you who want to create a deeper connection to Nature, a spiritual connection to Nature, or simply spend more time outdoors to always carry a bag with you. It could be a small rubbish bag, it could be a big one, you can carry a number of small ones, whatever is easy for you to carry around — and please, please, please pick up the rubbish, that you see as you walk through the forest. It is shocking the things that people leave behind.

You see the size of this forest: anyone who has come this deep into the forest — because you are quite far off the main trails and you are quite far away from the campsite and the car park — anyone who has come this deep into the forest is clearly someone who enjoys Nature, who enjoys being outdoors, who enjoys walking. Why then, would they leave their bottles, why would they leave their rubbish? We are shocked and disgusted and repulsed by the behavior of people that do this. It is a disrespect. It is a disrespect to Nature, it is a disrespect to the woods, it is a disrespect to all of the green things.

Plastic: we do not like it, we do not like it, we do not like it. Please help us to remove the plastic that some very disrespectful people leave behind. This is something that I feel very strongly about, and that is why I pointed out the fact that you needed to go back and pick up that bottle. This should not be optional. You have a bag, you know that you can pick things up, and if you do not currently carry a bag, then you start. It is very easy. It is very easy to do. You can carry the bag in your hand; you can hang it off your pack. You can do whatever you need to do, but please, please, please, I ask you to help clean the plastic out of the woodlands.

This sounds like a very simple thing, and it is. And perhaps once you start doing it you will think, "Ugh this is such a pain, I don't want to be carrying this trash around." But if you love Nature, if you love the outdoors, if you love us trees: please, please, help us. This is something that we cannot do. Only you can help pick up the rubbish that other people leave behind. This is a problem, it is unsightly, it is an energetic disturbance. Plastic does not belong here: if you like to carry it in, then you must carry it out.

We take offense when these things are left in our territory. We take offense when people have the interest to come to us and yet are so disrespectful that they leave these things behind.

Now, you may be thinking: perhaps people are not intentionally throwing their bottles behind, perhaps they have fallen out of their pack? Well then, I tell you: secure it on your packs or secure it inside of your pack. Put your bottles, your plastic, in a safe place in your pack, period. It is not that difficult. We see the things that you carry, we see all the different places that you have to carry your rubbish in and to carry your rubbish out. It is absolutely possible, it is absolutely doable.

You may sense my discontent, anger, irritation at this. This is something that I feel very strongly about, and this is something that we all feel strongly about, we trees — this is a great disrespect to the woodlands. It is a great disrespect not only to leave the plastic behind but to walk past it on the trail. It is so easy to step down and pick it up, and even if you don't have a bag with you, you can tuck it into your own pack.

So, I urge you, please: when you step on a bottle and you hear that plastic crunch, when you walk past a piece of plastic, please pick it up and carry it out with you even when it is not yours... **especially** when it is not yours. And I urge you to please start carrying a special bag with you, a rubbish bag that you can fill with plastic and take out with you.

Please, please, please, I urge you on behalf of all the trees: this is important. You may think that compared to the size of this forest, a bottle is such a small thing. It is not, it is not to us. So, if you would like to deepen your relationship with trees, with the woods, with Nature, you can start by helping to clean up because that is something that we cannot do; we can clean the air, but we cannot clean the plastic. We ask for your help in this task. It is of great importance to us.

This is all. Thank you.

# Experience

Put a small rubbish bag in your backpack so you can easily pick up garbage and plastic that you find in the woods. Do it: pick up the plastic and the rubbish that you find out in Nature. Treat this like it's not optional: that it's simply not possible to not pick up rubbish.

When you bring plastic bottles or other packaging into the woods, always be sure to put it safely inside your pack, and not in an outside pocket where it might fall off.

Never, ever intentionally leave your garbage and other plastics in Nature.

# Journal Prompts

## Before the Experience

* Do you carry a rubbish bag around with you when you go out into Nature?

* Do you ever pick up trash that other people have left behind?

* Are you willing to help to clean up the woods? If so, what are you willing to do? How often are you willing to do it? Are you willing to treat it like it's not an option to not pick things up?

## After the Experience

* How do you feel when you pick up rubbish in Nature? Are you happy to do it, or is it an annoyance to you?

* Have you made it a habit to clean up the woods and other natural spaces?

* What else could you do to help rid the woodlands of plastic and rubbish?

# SAVERNAKE QUEEN OAK

Do not mourn for me. Do not mourn for me. I am overjoyed to have spent the hundreds and hundreds of years that I have been in this forest. Look at me, you can see how old I am. And look at all the life there is on me: the ferns, the moss, all the living things on the forest floor below me, the fungus on my trunk, nestled amongst my old chunky bark. And look up and see what is left of my own life, tiny little branches. I am so old, and I am so pleased to have been standing here for so long. I am so pleased to have been given the recognition that I have been given: Original Queen Oak. You can see that my king has fallen and there is now a Replacement King Oak.

Everything has a cycle, everything has a lifespan, and mine is coming to an end. I have many years of life left in me, but not as many as I have lived. Now you heard my message, far back on the trail, even before you heard Pointing Oak's message.

My message, my story for you, is a story of joy because that is what I feel. That is what I feel having been here for so many hundreds of years: the joy of being a tree, the joy of being in this beautiful forest, surrounded by other trees, of other species, other oaks, chestnuts, surrounded by bracken, all the green things. Look at the beautiful blue sky that I have stretched my branches towards for hundreds of years. I feel such great joy to have been here on this Earth, in this place, in the form that I have taken of the majestic Queen Oak that I am. You know I have presence. You know I am beautiful, and you can imagine what I must have looked like a few decades before — perhaps even a hundred years ago.

And so that is what I want to speak to you about: find your joy.

If you want to connect more deeply with Nature, find your joy in Nature. Do you enjoy walking, do you enjoy running, do you enjoy cycling? What is it that you enjoy doing in Nature? Do you enjoy meditating in Nature? Do you enjoy just going to the park and having a cup of coffee or tea? Find your joy outdoors, find your joy with the trees, find your joy with all the living green things, find your joy and do it. Make it happen.

Make it happen on a regular basis: find your joy and **do it**. Give yourself permission to do the joyful outdoor things, which bring you a deep sense of happiness and connection, not only to the green things but to yourself. Find your joy and feel it, really **feel** it. And, as I said, give yourself permission to have these experiences, because sometimes people feel guilty. They come to the woods and they think, "I should be doing something else, I should be doing some work, I should be doing something with the family, I should do be doing emails, I should be paying bills." What they are really saying is: "I should be doing practical things."

Now, of course, you can bring your family to the woods if you like, but when you find your joy, perhaps it is being **alone** in the woods, perhaps it is being alone in the park. Whatever your joy is, give yourself permission to do it and make it a **priority** because it is an important part of you and your experience on this earth. It will help you to deepen your connection to yourself, it will help deepen your connection to your Higher Self, it will help you deepen your connection to Nature and all the green things, so you find your joy in Nature and you **do it**: free from guilt. Give yourself permission to do this.

How many trees have talked to you about the importance of slowing down? And perhaps your joy in Nature will be slowing down in Nature? Perhaps your joy will be jogging through Nature, cycling through Nature? There are different times for different things, so do not get this confused with other things that other trees have told you: there is a time for being still in Nature, there is a time for being quiet in Nature, and there is a time for living your joy in Nature and sometimes those things coincide and sometimes they do not. This is important for you to know, this task, this suggestion, this call to action of finding your joy in Nature is different from what other trees have told you. So, please experiment: find your joy.

Now if I were to ask you: what is your joy in Nature, what is your joy in the outdoors? How do you feel joy in the outdoors? What are the first things that come to mind? Write that down and if you think: "oh, I don't know, I don't know, how do I know that? That's such a big thing." Try. Experiment. Try one thing. Did you feel joy? If not, try another thing. Did you feel joy? If not, try another thing and keep trying, keep experimenting, keep playing, until you find that thing that is your joy in Nature and make it happen on a regular basis and really, really, feel that joy. It is **delicious**, is it not? Hmmm.

I am nearing the end of what I have to say to you and I am so pleased to have been able to share my story with you, my message for you, my task for you. My life has been full of great joy in this forest, I am so pleased, so pleased with my life. And I hope that you experience the same joy outdoors, in Nature, with the green things. Find your joy and experience it. Thank you.

# Experience

Find your joy in Nature: walking, running, cycling, meditating, or something else. Do it: make it happen on a regular basis, and really feel the joy in your body. Give yourself permission to have these experiences and make this a priority in your life.

If you haven't yet found your joy in Nature, try just one thing. Experiment. Keep trying things until you find it.

# Journal Prompts

## Before the Experience

* Have you found your joy in Nature? What is your joy in the outdoors? How do you feel joy in the outdoors?

* If you haven't found your joy in Nature, what types of outdoor activities are you drawn to doing?

* What new things do you feel like trying?

* How would you like to play in the outdoors?

## After the Experience

* What is your joy in Nature? Is it walking, meditating, cycling...or something else?

* How do you feel joy in the outdoors?

* Is your joy in doing these activities alone, or with others?

* If you have found your joy, do you actually make it a priority in your life?

* How often have you made it a priority to experience your joyful activities in Nature?

* How do you feel about doing it: do you feel guilty, or are you able to enjoy them free from guilt?

* Do you do it on a regular basis? If not, what can you do to make it happen more often?

# WESTERN HEMLOCK

I have something to say. We feel like we are looked down upon. We know that we are not native, we have been planted here. We are not native to this land, but we did not **ask** to be put here. We are not like other native trees in this wood, which would be allowed to live their full lives until they fall on their own or are struck by lightning, or are felled only because they are a danger to someone who is perhaps walking down the trail. We are here because we will be felled for our timber. You have seen the stacks and stacks of our relatives, trees like us. This is Forestry Commission land. This is what we are here for.

You may think us ugly: our bare trunks, little naked sticks stuck out of them like a skinny porcupine, just a bit of green on the upper top of the tree, and a wasteland down below. Broken branches, piles of needles, dry needles, and far off some baby hemlocks which add a bit of interest perhaps to the woods. We are not here for our beauty, we are not here because we belong here, we are not here because we are native. We are here because we have been planted, and we have a purpose. As long as you humans need timber, as long as you need wood for your furniture, as long as you need paper, as long as you need those things that are made of trees, we will be here, we will be planted. Not us exactly, but others like us. This is our future, this is our purpose. We are here to serve a purpose for your people.

We are very different from the other trees you have talked to. You have mostly been speaking to native British trees and we are not that, we know this. But, rather than feeling the disdain, the disrespect of people as they walk through us, as they walk through this part of the forest that is not made up of native trees, we would like to feel your respect. So, maybe we are not as beautiful as an old oak, or a holly, or a hawthorn, but we are providing a service. We are here to provide a service. We give you things that you use, and we give you things that you need, and we would like respect. And perhaps you can try to see the beauty, you can see the beauty in our service, you can see the beauty in our uniformity, you can see the beauty in the little baby trees that you find here and again underneath the taller trees, perhaps you can find the beauty in this non-native forest. It is not totally devoid of life: if you can hear a bird over there.

Another tree spoke to you earlier of the symphony of the leaves in the wind, and you can hear that now. We also contribute to the symphony. You can hear the rustling of our needles high above. Why then, can you not appreciate our beauty? You **can**. It is a change of attitude, it is a change of belief, it is a change of perspective. We would like to feel respect as you and others walk through this non-native forest, this commercial forest. The rustling of our needles in the wind, softly, look at our branches up high against the blue sky, we can be so graceful as we softly wave our branches in the breeze.

We are not ugly, we are trees, just like the native trees, and we are here to provide a service. Do not think that we would not prefer to live out a long life, as do the oaks, as do the yews. Do not think that. But this is our lot in life, this is who we are, this is what we are. This is our purpose in life, this is our path, and we have the same tree spirits as the other native trees that you have been speaking to. We are also individuals, although we may look the same to you, we ask that you please, please, look upon us with respect, look upon us as individuals, short-lived individuals, who will be providing a service to you and to other humans. We are here to serve.

And I hope that you will learn to appreciate us, to value us, to respect us. And when you walk through a commercial forest made up of non-native trees, see it as something different, not lesser-than, but different. Pay attention to attitude and how it changes as you walk through the rest of this commercial forest and other commercial forests in the future, we ask please that you do not see us as lesser than, but rather different. And that you see us as individuals and you see the service that we are here to provide for you because that is our role.

Thank you.

# Experience

Appreciate the beauty of all trees. Be thankful for them all, both native and non-native trees. See them as individuals.

Pay attention to your attitude as you walk through commercial forests and native forests. See the beauty in the forest, in their service, in their uniformity. Pay attention to the life in the forest: what birds can you hear?

Do what you need to do to change your perspective on commercial forests: feel respect for these trees; show your respect for them.

Remember to thank the trees that have given their lives for the products that we use: furniture, paper, cardboard, etc. They are providing a service to us; thank them for their service.

# Journal Prompts

## Before the Experience

🌿 How did you feel about non-native forests before reading this chapter?

🌿 Were you aware of having less respect for non-native trees, or was this not an issue for you?

## After the Experience

🌿 What was it like to visit the commercial forest?

🌿 Were you able to put any negative attitudes aside and appreciate their beauty?

🌿 What is your current attitude toward commercial forests and non-native trees?

🌿 How do you feel about giving thanks for the products that we use that come from trees? Have you started doing this?

🌿 Has it made you more aware of the origin of these products?

🌿 Has it made you more aware of your consumption of these products?

🌿 Have you changed your habits around using paper and cardboard products?

# KING OF LIMBS

You were very pleased to see me and then when you came inside and sat down, you felt as though there was no story, that there was not going to be a story. My story is to tell you that there are some places like this where you feel a kind of bubble of energy. It could be in the belly of an old tree, like me, it could be a place like a sacred spring, or any of the special places where you have felt that you step inside a place and it is almost like you are cut off from the rest of the world, separate, almost as if you are in a different dimension. These are the places where you must sit awhile: just sit, you can do anything. You don't have to observe, you don't have to experience, you don't have to be silent; you could look at things on your phone, you could read a book, you could listen to music.

It doesn't matter what you do, because when you go to these places you are there to receive energy. This could be healing energy, this could be vitalizing energy — it is the energy of that place that you are there to receive. And sometimes it is best if your mind is not active, so you may think: "oh those are the places where it is good to go and meditate, and focus on the energy, and be very serious" — but not necessarily. These are places where it is often good for you to do what you just did when you sat in here, which was to look at a map and plan your route back. These are places for you to read, places for you to keep your conscious mind engaged so that the energy can slip in and swirl around and do its job in your physical body. Of course, you can do whatever you choose. I am just here to tell you that this is one of those places: you feel it, you know it.

So, stay as long as you feel drawn to, whether it is one minute, or five minutes, half an hour, an hour, or longer. When you start to feel restless, then you know that it is time to leave because you have received what you were meant to receive. Do what you need to do to stay warm, to stay cool, depending on what time of the year it is: put on an extra layer of clothing, take off an extra layer, do what you need to do to be comfortable during the time that you will be in these special bubbles of energy.

Do what you need to do to keep your mind busy, and just allow yourself to soak up the energy, consciously or unconsciously, of these special bubble sites. There is really not much more that I can tell you about this: just be open to feeling those special places, and you know that you are there when you are drawn to a certain place and you sit down, and you feel like you are in a different space, most likely there is some kind of protection, or filter, between you and the rest of the world; you hear the leaves rustling in the trees but sounds really, really, far off. It doesn't sound like it is right next to you, that you are in that part of the woods. These are the places where you can receive great energy, and again, you do not need to do anything, you just need to be there.

So we encourage you to keep your mind busy when you go to these places, don't over think things, don't make it out to be more serious, or more spiritual, or more whatever than it is. It is just is what it is, it is just energy, and it flows — just doing its thing, no big deal. But I encourage you to sit a while in these places, and you will know how long. Thank you.

# Experience

Find the places in Nature that feel like a special bubble. Open up to receive the energy of the place. Keep your mind distracted by looking at a map or your phone or by writing in this workbook. Stay as long as you like and know that when you begin to feel restless it is time to move on. Remember to give thanks to the place for the experience, and for whatever else you may receive.

# Journal Prompts

## Before the Experience

* Have you ever felt a strange energy like I did when I was at King of Limbs? How have you responded?

* If you've never experienced something like this, what do you think you would have done if you had felt the strange energy I experienced near the old oak?

* Would you have stuck around and investigated? Would you have tried to see what was there, or feel into its energy more?

* Would you ever return to a place where you felt something so strange and uncomfortable? Why, or why not?

## After the Experience

* Were you able to identify any special bubble-like places in Nature?

* Were you able to distract your mind so you could more easily receive the energy?

* Were you able to easily feel when it was time to move on? What was the signal that you got?

* Do you feel like you have to do something special or important when you sit in places that feel like an energy bubble, or are you content to simply sit there and do whatever you feel like?

# THE FOUR KNIGHTS

We are The Four Knights. As you can see, we are four trees that have grown together in a cluster, and we are here to represent the multi-layered soul that we are and that all living beings are. Your soul has traveled through many lifetimes, and your soul has chosen to experience very specific things in each lifetime. Your soul has chosen specific challenges for each lifetime, and it has chosen specific things it would like to experience in each lifetime, in order to grow and evolve into the multi-layered soul that it strives to be. And this is why sometimes things are difficult, sometimes things are challenging, these are things that your soul has chosen to experience, to help your soul to grow.

Now, oftentimes, we see people getting caught up in their current lifetime, in their current struggles, in their current situations, while failing to see the bigger picture: the overarching theme of what they have chosen to learn and how they have chosen to grow. And oftentimes people fail to understand that they have chosen the situations that they are experiencing in this lifetime.

Now, one of the big challenges in life is to put your current lifetime, and personality, and challenges, a bit to the side so that you can integrate all of your lessons, all of your learnings, all of your richness of previous lifetimes and bring all of that into this current lifetime. This can be a challenge because it is so easy to get caught up in everyday life difficulties, in everyday life struggles, in everyday interactions with other people. But there is more to life than that, and the sooner you can bring in all of the gifts from your previous lifetimes, all the things you have learned from your previous lifetimes — the sooner that you can bring those lessons into your current life — the sooner you will begin to experience flow and ease and a sort of settling into this lifetime. This is something that you must remember from lifetime to lifetime, to lifetime, and yet you forget.

Now, for us trees it is easier because we hold a deep connection to the land, a deep connection to the other trees: we always have a network, we always have access to experiences from previous lifetimes. It is not so easy for you humans, and yet it is possible, and it is doable, and you can do it. So we are here to suggest that you give it a try: we suggest that you bring these learnings from your previous lifetimes into this life. Now, the first step is becoming aware that this is a thing: that this is a possibility, and that this is something that you can do. The next step is to set the intention: to set the intention to the Universe that you are willing to do this work, that you are ready, willing, and able to bring all of the multi-layers of your previous lifetimes into this lifetime and that you are ready, willing, and able to integrate them and live from this place of soul being.

This is the best way to start this path. The more you open yourself up to this possibility, the easier it will be for this to happen. The more you ask for help from the beings around you, whether it is the Nature spirits, angels, whatever you choose to ask for help with, the easier it will be to integrate these parts of you, because these are all parts of you: these are all multi-layered parts of your being, even though you may feel that you currently do not have access to them.

So walk the land, meditate, slow down, do whatever it is that you need to do to connect with yourself, and when you do so, set the intention to connect with all the multilayered dimensions of yourself, of your soul, over all the years and years and years and millennia of lifetimes. We ask that you do this work, because the more people that do this work, the faster your society, the faster the energy will evolve on this planet, and that will be a better place for you, and that will be a better place for us, and for all living beings, including the earth.

Now more than ever it is easy to do this work. It is easy to walk this path. It starts by setting the intention because you are already aware of this, we ask that you give it a try.

That is all.

# Experience

Bring the learnings from previous lifetimes into this lifetime. First, become aware that this is possible. Next, set the intention to do so. Ask for help from Nature, or from whatever higher power you recognize, or the beings around you, including Nature spirits, angels, or whomever you choose. Remember to give thanks for the help you receive.

Slow down and connect with yourself. Set the intention to connect with all the multilayered dimensions of yourself across all your lifetimes.

# Journal Prompts

## Before the Experience

* Do you believe in the possibility of past lifetimes? If not, why not?

* If so, do you believe that you can bring everything you've learned from past lives into your current life?

* Are you willing to set the intention to bring that knowledge and wisdom into this current lifetime?

* How do you think it would change your life if you could remember all the wisdom that you have accumulated throughout numerous lifetimes?

* Do you think that having this knowledge would lead you to make different decisions in life?

* How do you think it might change the way you feel about things?

## After the Experience

* Did you ask for help from a higher power to make it easier for you to bring the learnings from past lives into your current life? If so, which one?

* Has anything shifted in your life since trying this? Have you felt any changes? Received any insights?

* What can you do on an ongoing basis to try to bring into this lifetime your wisdom and knowledge from previous lifetimes?

# TWIN SYCAMORES

There is a time and there is a place for everything. And sometimes you will feel satisfied by the timing you experience in your life, and sometimes you will feel frustrated and feel dissatisfied. Sometimes you want things to happen, specific things at a specific time. Sometimes it is possible, often it is not. You must learn the delicate balance between wanting, setting goals, taking action, planning to do things, to make these things happen in your life, and balance that with trusting that everything will happen at the perfect time for you and that you will experience the perfect experiences that you have come here, and chosen to come here, to experience.

Sometimes these will be enjoyable, sometimes they will not. If you take advantage of these experiences, if you take advantage of all of these experiences, they can all be very useful in your growth. Oftentimes people fall into the victim trap of feeling sorry for themselves, and this does not serve you. So my lesson for you, my story for you, my message for you, is to pay more attention to the seasons. Every year it is more or less the same, every year you have more or less the same seasons, sometimes they start earlier and sometimes they start later. Sometimes one season is longer, another season is shorter. There are variations: it is not exactly the same, but you can expect winter, spring, summer and fall, every single year. There are cycles; these are things that you can expect. These are things that we can expect as trees.

Observe the changes, know that nothing lasts forever, and see if you can relax, and flow. Relax and flow through the seasons, relax and flow through the changes, relax and flow through the experiences of your life. Let go of worry, nothing lasts forever. Pay attention to the things that you want to experience and focus on those; know and trust that they will come when it is their season and it is their time. And the season for the changes, these things that you want to experience, may or may not be aligned with the timing that you wish for, and this is okay. Relax and flow into the changes. Focus on the changes that you want to experience and relax, do not be too — we do not want to say committed — do not be too **stuck** on any one idea, because there may be something better for you, there may be something more satisfying for you to experience that you have not even yet conceived. And it might be that by taking action toward the thing that you want, that a new thing opens up to you, in different timing, or in the same timing.

Relax, and allow yourself to flow through the seasons of your life focusing on what you choose to experience and knowing that surprises may happen, surprises may come, unexpected things may occur, and this is all right. This is to be expected. This is to be relished. This is to be savored. Oftentimes people do not welcome surprises, and they are disappointed by them, they are frustrated by them because it is not what they expected, it is not what they wanted. Again, I tell you: relax and flow through the seasons of your life and open your arms to the unexpected experiences. Ask what you might learn from this experience, what you might learn from not having the experience that you wanted instead. And going into Nature, and sitting in Nature, not just walking but stopping and sitting will help you to slow down and integrate the gifts of these experiences.

Allow yourself to slow down.

I know I am not the first tree to tell you this. You may find yourself hearing the same, or similar messages, from different trees, because we see that this is very much needed in your world. Flow, flow, flow — gently, not violently — your life does not need to be a river of rapids; it could be a gently flowing stream. And you may find flowing through your life as a gently flowing stream to be more satisfying, more manageable. Slow down and go out into Nature and observe the changing of the seasons.

It is fall now and I have lost most of my leaves: there are some falling from my branches as you record this, as you sit here, receiving my message. The ground underneath my branches is carpeted with crispy leaves, some of them freshly fallen, some of them dried and brown. We are approaching winter, then spring, then summer, and it all begins again, it all continues. It is a cycle, as your life is a cycle, and the more you pay attention to the cycles in your life, the easier it will be to flow: to flow through the cycles of your life, and to flow through your experiences, and to appreciate each and every one, even the unexpected experiences.

This is all.

# Experience

Pay attention to the seasons and observe the changes you see in Nature.

Know that there is a time and there is a place for everything. Learn to balance wanting, setting goals, taking action, and planning with trusting that everything will happen at the perfect time for you and that you will have the perfect experiences for you.

Pay attention to the things you want to experience in your life and know and trust that the best things will come to you at the best possible time. Take action toward the things that you want and be open to new experiences coming to you.

Relax and flow through unexpected changes. Expect the unexpected, and appreciate each and every experience.

# Journal Prompts

## Before the Experience

✹ Do you believe in the concept of Divine timing?

✹ Are you good at relaxing and flowing through the ups and downs of life?

✹ If so, how do you think this benefits you?

✹ If not, how do you think your life might be different if you did allow yourself to relax and flow? Do you think it might make things easier?

✹ When you look back over the years of your life, can you see how everything fell into place, even if it didn't make sense at the time?

✹ Can you see how things that were difficult or painful actually taught you valuable life lessons?

✹ If not, are you willing to spend some time now looking for what those lessons might be?

## After the Experience

✹ What have you learned from paying attention to the seasons and observing the changes throughout the year?

✹ Has it helped you to be more accepting of unexpected changes in your life?

✹ Has it helped you to flow through the cycles of your own life?

✹ Do you trust that things will come to you with the best possible timing, even though it may not be the timing you prefer?

*If Trees Could Talk – A Companion Workbook*

# THE SOMERSET FOUR

**B**e spontaneous.

Do whatever pops into your mind.

Do not be worried of what others might think, and do not be worried by what others may think of you: hugging a tree, or sitting against a tree, or however it is that you choose to engage with the trees. Really **feel** what you need, feel what you need, feel into the experience of interacting with the trees. You just went up to the oak, in the middle of our triangle, and you hugged the oak because you felt drawn to do so, but you **really** hugged the oak, you felt like you were hugging a living being. It wasn't just the intellectual act of putting your arms around a tree: you felt it. In the same way that you felt it, other people can feel this too.

You should know by now that each tree has a different personality, a different energy, a different way of being. Go to the trees that you are most drawn to and really, really, feel them, feel their energy. You did not intend to feel that tree's energy or have such a good hug of the tree when you went up to it; you felt drawn to hugging the tree and so you did. And this is what we encourage everyone to do. Do what you feel drawn to do, and linger, and relax, and give yourself permission to spend time engaging with the tree. To spend time **feeling** into the tree, and sense what happens.

When you went to the first yew, you felt that you needed to sit down with your back against its trunk and you felt that energy seep into your body from the tree, and you felt that you had to encourage yourself to relax, so you focused on relaxing all the different parts of your body. You closed your eyes and you gave yourself permission to relax and you felt that energy flowing into your body from the yew, and you felt it, and you felt it, until it was as if a tap had been turned off and you get the sense that it was enough, that it was time to move on and so you did.

And then you came to me, and you can sense the energy flowing into your back from my trunk. You will know when it is time to get up and leave, and if you do not, there is no matter, there is no prescribed length of time to engage with the trees. What we encourage you to do is to give yourself permission to relax, and to feel into each tree, trust your intuition, trust your gut, when it tells you **how** to engage with the tree, whether it is hugging it, or sitting up against it, or any of the other things that you have learned in these stories from the trees that you have already heard.

Give yourself permission to relax and receive, relax and receive, for we have good things to give you. And if you stay too long or if you stay not enough time, that is okay. The more you do this, the easier it will get, the more you will trust yourself, and the more you will know. The important thing is to start. So the next time you are out in the woods, pay attention to what you feel drawn to do, and give yourself permission to just relax and receive; relax and receive and **feel**. Feel what it is that you are receiving from the tree, feel what it is that you are giving the tree. It is a symbiotic relationship, you might call it: relax and connect, relax and connect.

Enjoy, and know that when you go out into Nature and you receive from the trees, and you receive from the spirits of the land, know that you will need integration time — know that you will need time to process all that you have received and let it sink into your body and spirit and soul. You may not understand the energy that you have received and that is fine, there is no need to intellectualize what happens when you receive from the trees, when you receive from Nature. The important thing is that you allow yourself to receive and that you allow yourself to integrate that which you have received. This may take time, you may feel tired, hungry, needing to rest afterward, or you may not notice anything. Just be aware that time is needed, so you may find that your experiences with the trees, your experiences with Nature, go in spurts; you may find yourself very drawn to be out in Nature, and then you might find that you don't feel like going out for several days, or several weeks, this is natural, this is a natural cycle. You receive and then you integrate, you receive and then you integrate, you receive and then you integrate. This is all natural, this is all normal. Go with the flow, do what you feel you need to do.

This is all.

# Experience

Be spontaneous when interacting with the trees. Do whatever you feel drawn to do, whatever you feel you need: sit against the tree, hug the tree, whatever. Relax and receive. Feel whatever it is you are giving the tree and receiving from the tree. Relax and connect. Spend some time engaging with the tree, feeling into the tree. Remember to give thanks to the trees for the experience.

Allow yourself integration time for what you have received.

# Journal Prompts

## Before the Experience

🌳 Do you experience ebbs and flows of doing inner work, or do you experience this in other areas of your life?

🌳 Are you aware of the cycles in your life?

🌳 Are there times when you feel really drawn to spend more time in Nature, and times when you don't?

🌳 What are the times of the year that you prefer to be outdoors?

## After the Experience

🌳 Were you able to allow yourself to be spontaneous when interacting with the trees?

🌳 How did you choose to engage with them?

🌳 Were you able to allow yourself to relax and receive?

🌳 Did you feel a sense of give and take with the tree?

🌳 How did you feel while doing this activity?

🌳 Did you notice if you were tired, hungry, or thirsty afterward?

🌳 Did you remember to allow yourself integration time for the energy, wisdom, or whatever it was that you received from the tree?

🌳 How has this activity changed how you engage with Nature in general?

# RAILWAY OAK

**I**t was summertime when you first realized that I was in your book. You were out on a walk, on a warm sunny day, clear skies — much like this day, but warm instead of cold. And I said to you: **I am in your book**. And you said you would come back. Many months have gone by since that day, and I know you have kept me in the back of your mind, and perhaps even chided yourself for not returning sooner.

I know it is important for me to say, to tell you now, that everything has its time, and everything has its place, and it is important that you are here **now** in the chill of winter to receive my story. As you look up into my branches you can see that there are very few leaves still left on them. I do have more leaves than my neighbor oak, but there are not many left, they are scattered on the ground, all around me and I am going into that dormant time, that time of slowing down during the cold months. And the reason that it is important that you are here during this time is because I know other trees have spoken to you about the seasons, and the cycles, and the turning of the year, and I fear that this is something that you humans must hear time and time again in order for it to sink in. So, do not be bothered that my story may be similar to other stories that you have read, or received, or heard; because you may often sense a need to go within, to slow down, to quiet during these cold winter months. You may sense that you do not feel like going outdoors and walking and being active. You feel the need to be alone and silent, perhaps meditate, or read, or journal, or do the inner work. And this is fine, this is okay, this is appropriate.

We trees know that you people feel the need to go, go, go, and that is sometimes appropriate, and sometimes not. Every time there is a period of go, go, go there must be a time of rest, rest, rest. A time of action, a time of integration. A time of movement, a time of peace. And winter may be that time for some of you; it may not be for others. You may find that you require several periods of slowing down during the year, and this is fine.

We sense that this is a struggle for you people, and you feel that you must always be productive, that you must always be taking action, that you must always be doing something, you must always be working towards your goals, your things that you want to do, things that you want to achieve. Sometimes what is needed is to just **be**, to just be who you are, where you are, what you are, how you are, right now in this moment, on this day. To relax, to rest, to integrate, but to be **aware** of who you are and what you are, and what you have, right now in this moment, instead of always looking to the future — to what you want to have, to what you want to be, to what you want to do.

Be present in **today**.

We know that many people talk about being present in the moment and that can be very challenging for people. So, what I would suggest is to be present in today: what do you have today? What are you doing today? What are you being today? Who are you today? Forget the past, forget the future, just look at today. This period of time between the time you woke up this morning, and the time you will be going to bed this evening. Look at that, feel that, be that. It is just today.

Be grateful for what you have today. Be thankful for who you are today. Give gratitude for what you are doing today, for what you are capable of doing, for what you are able to do. Be thankful for having the time and the space in your life to do the things that you are doing today. Whatever that is, even if it is something that you do not enjoy doing, even if it is something that you need to do later and you wish you could procrastinate, or you want to procrastinate. Be grateful and focus on today.

All you have is today. We know this may sound overused perhaps, the concept that all you have is the present moment: the past no longer exists, the future does not yet exist, and yet they do, because if you step into your multi-dimensional self, everything exists all at once. That can be overwhelming, so we ask you to focus on today, how do you feel today? Not how do you want to feel — but how do you feel? Not what do you want to do today — but what are you doing today? Not who do you want to be — but who are you today? Who are you being today? Let go of wants, let go of wishes, let go of goals, let go of dreams, let go of visions. And practice this every once in a while, I do not say: practice it every day — you can if you want, of course, but just try it for once. Practice just being in today, being present in today.

This is something that you may wish to journal about: some of you may feel it easier to put your thoughts on paper, rather than to simply think them, or live them, or experience them. You might want to journal at various points throughout the day, or in the morning, or at the end of the day, to reflect on your experience of just being in today. Do whatever works for you, but we encourage you to try this just once, just once, and then pay attention to how it affects your life. What has changed as a result of this experience, and then decide whether you want to experience it again — this exercise of just being in today.

There is so much, so much focus on the past, so much focus on the future, I strongly encourage you to be in today, to live today, fully, in today. I wish you luck.

That is all.

# Experience

Become aware of where you are in the cycles and the turning of the year: you may feel the need to go within in the winter, or spend more time outdoors in the spring, or be more active in the summer. Balance doing with being; action with rest.

Be present in today: journal at various points throughout the day, or in the morning, or at the end of the day, to reflect on your experience of just being in today. Do this in a separate journal, or here in this workbook.

Be grateful for what you have today. Be thankful for who you are today. Give gratitude for what you are doing today, for what you are capable of doing, for what you are able to do. Be thankful for having the time and the space in your life to do the things that you are doing today.

Pay attention to how this practice affects your life. Look at what has changed as a result of this experience, and then decide whether you want to experience it again.

# Journal Prompts

## Before the Experience

* Do you find it easy to focus on today, or do you find it difficult?
* Do you ever journal on what happens to you each day?
* How do you think that journaling about each day might be beneficial to your life?
* If you do not currently engage in this practice, is this something that you might be willing to try?

## After the Experience

* If you gave this experience a try, how did it affect your life? What things did you notice?
* What changed in your life as a result of doing this work?
* Is it something you want to continue?
* Do you ever do gratitude work? If not, would you like to try it?
* If you engage in gratitude work, how has it changed your life? What's different for you?

# BEARE GREEN OAK

I will not tell you what so many other trees have told you, which is **slow down, you move too fast**. But what I will tell you is that things often take — they often require — time and space. This is a lesson that you have learned, that you may continue to learn, but not everything happens in the timeframe that you would desire it. Let's take this book, perhaps you would have wanted to receive all the stories of the trees in one month, or in one season. But it has taken almost the course of the entire year to receive these stories: there have been different trees, in different places, and it has been important to receive different stories at different times of the year, as you have just learned.

This is just one more perfect example of how some things — **all** things perhaps — require time and space. And you must give yourself time and space if you want to achieve the things you want to achieve; if you want to experience the things that you want to experience. Some things take time. Some things take a longer time than you would expect, some things take less time than you would expect. This is all normal, this is all okay.

The important thing is to recognize — to recognize that things take time. When you slow down, and you give yourself the space to open up and receive, to open up and experience, to open up and feel, this will lead you to new experiences, to new things, to new ways of being. And this requires space. And what we mean by space is slowing down, sitting still, just being, quieting your mind, journaling, meditating, sitting in silence, being still. And opening up to receive; to receive guidance from your higher self, to receive messages, to receive downloads, and this will help you connect to yourself, this will help you trust yourself, this will help you cultivate that inner-compass that can be life-changing.

This takes time, this takes space. And this is why my message is to remind you to give yourself space — alone time, self-care time — in which you can be quiet and be still, and relax and receive and connect. Give yourself permission to give yourself space. Give yourself permission to give yourself time. Give yourself permission to be still.

You may feel that stillness time is lost time — wasted time — because you are not being productive. On the contrary, stillness time is **every bit as productive** as doing time. Give yourself permission to slow down, and be still, and make space.

You may feel restless, you may want to move, you may want to get going onto your next thing. So, allow yourself to ease into this practice of being still and giving yourself space, and see if you can change your perspective. See if you can change your perspective so that you see stillness time as productive time, or whatever word you need it to be — valuable time, worthy time, useful time. Use whatever word you need to fully appreciate the value of this time and space that you give yourself.

It is important to give yourself time and space without sensory input, so you may think of doing a guided meditation, and while these are good, it is also good to be still without this type of auditory input. You may find it useful to do sensory deprivation activities such as a floatation tank, a place where you can go in silence, in peace, in darkness, and just rest and relax and just be. There are many ways that you can do this. You can simply meditate in the dark and silence at home. Whatever feels right for you. We encourage you to be still in all your senses, not just movement, but to be in silence and stillness and darkness — this will help you connect to yourself, your higher self, your inner compass, and it will open you up to new ways of being.

That is all.

# Experience

Recognize that things require time and space; give yourself the time and space you need to do the things you want to achieve. Understand that stillness time can be every bit as productive as doing time.

Give yourself space: alone time or self-care time, in which you can be quiet and be still and relax and receive and connect. Give yourself time and space without any sensory input (such as guided meditations, though there is a time and space for those). Consider visiting a floatation tank or meditating in a completely dark place.

# Journal Prompts

## Before the Experience

* Do you find it easy to sit in stillness, or is it a challenge for you?

* If it's something you find difficult, what are some ways you could add a bit of stillness to your life, even if it's just a few minutes?

* When would be a good time of day to do this?

* Do you make self-care a priority?

* What kinds of things help you to feel like you're caring for yourself? Reading a book? Taking a bath? Sitting in the garden?

* Do you get enough self-care time in your life?

* If not, when can you add a bit of self-care to your life, even if it's just a few minutes?

## After the Experience

* If you have tried making stillness a part of your life, is this something you would you like to continue?

* Would you like to do it more often? Or for longer periods of time?

* What activities would you add to your self-care routine?

# WOLVENS LANE BEECH

I would say I am surprised to see you. And yet, I knew I would see you again, and that you would come back to collect my story. You have walked by me many times since the first time I told you that I would be in your book, and that I had a story for you. And it is not by accident that you have returned to me near the end of the year, after receiving so many other tree stories.

Many of the trees have been talking to you about slowing down, sitting, being still. This is all sound advice. And yet, I am here to talk to you about the journey. For this book has been a journey. It has been a journey for you as the collector of stories, and it is has been a journey for you as the reader of the stories. And it has been a journey for me and for all the trees. So I am here to remind you, at risk of sounding hmm...cliché, that life is a journey, that everything is a journey.

I know that the previous trees have spoken to you of things taking time and this is true, and we know that this can be frustrating to you. I encourage you to see life as a journey and everything as a journey: a journey of personal development, a journey of achieving your goals, a journey of working towards your dreams. So often you people focus on the end result, so often you focus on what you will get at the **end** of the journey. I am here to remind you to focus on the path, to focus on the trail, to focus on all the little bits in between.

It should be easy for you to understand this because when you go on your walks, the focus of the walk is not getting to the end: it is enjoying the path, it is enjoying the journey, it is enjoying the experience of the walk. So, why then can you not apply this to your life? To the rest of your life? To all the other things that you do?

I am going to say the words that you have heard so many times this year: slow down. Slow down and experience the path; slow down and experience the journey; slow down and experience the freedom of each step as it takes you forward. Or backwards. Or sideways. Or wherever you are going. Truly experience the path, truly experience each day, truly experience the process of getting from where you are to where you want to be. And be open to the fact that the destination may change. It may change once, it may change twice, it may change many, many times, along your path, along your journey. And this is fine. This is good, this is desirable.

It is desirable that you should be flexible, to flow with the changes of life. And yet that is not possible if you are only fixated on the end. And so I encourage you to focus instead on each single step. Each step on the way, each step on the path, each step on the journey. Take your steps one by one.

Focus on each step. Experience each step. Relish each step. Live each step.

Rather than seeing these steps as the necessary bother of getting from here to there, relish them as the main dish, the main course, the main part of your experience.

You have seen, when you go on your longer walking journeys, that when you get to the end,

*If Trees Could Talk – A Companion Workbook*                                                    **197**

it is not what you expected: it is not what you hoped for, there are no fireworks and parties and celebrations. Yes, of course you can have your own personal celebration and perhaps you should, if you want to.

But on your longer walks you have seen that each step of the way, each day of the trail, is the core part of the experience, it is the main course, and you can apply that concept to the rest of your life. Each step of the way being the main course of your life, and not the end, not the destination, because your life will be full of destinations. It is all a path of cycles and returns. So it is vital that you enjoy each step of the way. Relish it.

You may be wondering: that sounds so easy, how do I do that?

It can take time out of each day, in the morning, in the afternoon, in the evening. In the morning and evening would be good, or perhaps just once a day, to do a daily review. What did you experience that day? What path were you walking? What actions did you take? How did you feel? What did you do? How did the steps that you took today contribute to your path, to your journey, to your experience of life?

You can spend some time reflecting or you can write them down in your journal, but do this once a day, whenever you feel is best. You could do it in the morning, reflecting on the previous day. You can do it in the afternoon, reflecting on the previous 24 hours. You can do it in the evening reflecting on all the events that have occurred in your waking hours.

But focus on those steps, write them down in your journal, reflect on them. Focus on the steps that you took on your life's path, today. What they gave you, what they did for you and how you felt about them and how they contributed to your overall journey.

Try this and see how things change for you. Pay attention to the changes. Pay attention to how you feel differently. Pay attention to how you experience life differently.

Thank you. That is all.

# Experience

Take time out of each day, in the morning, in the afternoon, or in the evening, to do a daily review: spend some time reflecting or journaling. You can do it in your personal journal, or here in the workbook. Focus on the steps that you took on your life's path on this day. What these steps gave you, what they did for you, how you felt about them, and how they contributed to your overall journey.

# Journal Prompts

## Before the Experience

- Do you find it easy to focus on the journey, or are you so focused on the end result that you forget to enjoy the path to get there?

- What can you do to truly relish each step of your journey?

- What can you do to enjoy each step on your path to achieve your goals?

- How do you feel about doing a daily review where you write about your day and how it contributed to your journey in life?

- How do you think that might change your life?

- When would be a good time to do this?

## After the Experience

- If you tried doing this daily review as it relates to your life's journey, what did it give you?

- What new things did you become aware of as a result of doing this work?

- How did it make you feel?

- Is this something you would like to continue?

# NEWLANDS CORNER YEW

**I knew** you would be back.

The other trees weren't so sure, but I knew I had given the task to the right person. And I also know that this project — this book — is not what you expected. I know that it turned out to be very, very, different — different types of stories; different focus; different energy; different feel — to what you expected, to what you thought you would receive.

And this was an important part of your path, an important part of your journey, and an important part of the story, the overarching story for your readers, because sometimes things aren't what we expect, sometimes things don't work out the way we wanted them to, and sometimes we question: are we on the right path? Am I going in the right direction? Did I make the right decision? Am I where I am supposed to be right now, or should I be here, or should I be there, or should I be further...further ahead on my path?

And this is normal, and this is natural, and this is all a part of you trusting yourself, learning to trust yourself, and learning to be flexible and fluid and flow with the changes, to flow with the unexpected differences and to trust that all is well, while at the same time, working to achieve the things that you want to achieve, doing the things that you want to do, but having that flexibility, that flow, so that when things aren't what you expected you can flow around them, flow up over them, but envision yourself like the water, the water that rains down upon us, the water that flows through a stream. Moving water always finds its way, it always finds its path, it creates its own path.

There are many lessons to be learned from Nature. In this book you have learned from trees, and we have much wisdom, and if you were to write another book and another and another and continue to collect the stories of trees, you would have so many different messages and lessons and perspectives and things that you can do, and things that you can try, and it would be endless — it would be as many trees as there are on this planet, but that is not necessary. If you feel drawn to do so, you **can** do so, in the same way, that you can, on your walks, reach out to trees, ask them if they have a message for you, and receive their message. And you can simply receive. It does not need to be made into anything; it does not need to be Volume II of this book. It does not need to be an encyclopedia of all the tree stories — it can simply be a message for you...or not.

You could take the list of activities and suggestions that the trees in this book have given you, and you could do them all and cross them off on your list, or you could do none of them, or you could do some of them. Or you could create your own things based on what you feel like doing, how you feel like connecting with the trees, how you feel like connecting with Nature, or even new ideas of things that new trees give you. You can do whatever you want, whatever feels right for you, there are no prescriptions, there are no laws, there are no shoulds, there are only coulds. You could do this, or you could do that. You might do this; you might do that.

There are only possibilities: possibilities for you on your journey to connecting with the trees, to connecting with Nature in all of its forms, in all of its realms, connecting with the plant realm and the animal realm and the mineral realm. You may feel more drawn to one than to the other. I suspect if you are reading this book it is because you feel drawn to the plant realm, to the green things, to the green spirits, and this is fine, and this is good, and we encourage this. And we also encourage connection with the animal realm and the mineral realm, because it is all valid and it is all good and it is all part of Nature, and it is all part of the ways that you can connect with yourself, through connecting with Nature. And the more that you slow down, and the more that you slow your speed, and the more that you learn to be still, in your life and in Nature, the easier it will be for you to connect with yourself and the easier it will be for you to build that inner trust, that inner sense of self-love and acceptance that some of the trees have spoken to you about.

I am so pleased that you have gone on this journey that I sent you on, and I am so pleased that you are sharing this message with others, and I would encourage you — readers of this book — to please, please, please, share this message with other people, in whatever way comes naturally to you. You can write about this in your journal, and get your clarity, and then talk about it with friends, you can blog about it, and you can do whatever feels right for you. But please, I encourage you: if you have felt touched by Nature, if there is something that you read in this book, or through something else, please share this message with others. Because the more people that get out in Nature, and the more people that connect with Nature and really build a relationship with Nature, the more we will experience harmony on this planet because, as you can see from this book, this has very much been about building a relationship with Nature in the same way that you would build a relationship with another human, or another animal.

This is a journey of building relationships, and any stories that you can tell people about building relationships with Nature will help others to build a relationship with Nature; and the more humans that deepen their connection with Nature and their relationships with the elements of Nature, the healthier this planet will be, the happier this planet will be; and it will lift the energy of this earth and all of the living beings that inhabit it. It will lift the energy up, into a new state of health and wellbeing and enlightenment and lightness of being and light energy.

We are here, and we are waiting. We will always be waiting.

And so we send this out to you as an invitation: an invitation to connect with us, to build a relationship with us, and in doing so to raise the vibration of the energy of this planet, as you help yourself you will be helping every living thing on this earth. That may seem impossible, it may seem strange, difficult, yet it is true. By helping yourself you will — little by little — raise the vibration of everything here and the more people that do this, the more people that step into this, the more people that walk this path, bit by bit, little by little, everything will shine, and you will turn up the volume, the brightness, of the light that shines across this planet and things will begin to heal, wellness, balance, and equilibrium will be restored. This is possible, little by little, bit by bit, with everyone doing their bit, everyone doing their part.

I hope you have enjoyed this journey and I hope you continue to take steps on this path, connecting with Nature, building relationships with Nature. It has been a pleasure to have had my part in stimulating this adventure, sparking the first step on this journey. I am so grateful that you have joined me, and us the trees, we thank you, thank you, thank you, thank you.

That is all.

# Experience

Share the message with others of your experience of reading this book and of connecting with Nature.

Build relationships: any stories that you can tell people about building relationships with nature will help others to build a relationship with Nature.

Be grateful for all that you receive: remember to give thanks to Nature, to the plant realm, to the trees for your experiences and for the help that they give you. Whenever you ask for help, always be sure to give thanks.

# Journal Prompts

## After the Experience

- 🌱 What have you learned from experimenting with these different ways of connecting with the trees?
- 🌱 What have you learned from spending more time in Nature and actually connecting with the trees?
- 🌱 How has your life changed?
- 🌱 Do you feel that it's deepened your connection with yourself?
- 🌱 What would you tell a friend who was interested in spending more time in Nature?
- 🌱 What stories of your own would you tell them? What experiences would you share?
- 🌱 What other ways would you like to engage with Nature?
- 🌱 Would you like to spend more time in Nature? How can you make this happen?

# PART
# THREE

# Resources

## Learn to Channel

* Cara Wilde's Channel Your Guide online course https://carawilde.com/channel-your-guide/

* Opening to Channel: Connecting with Your Guide Audio Course by Sanaya Roman and Duane Packer https://www.orindaben.com/catalog/prodno/C101/

* Lisa Wechtenhiser's WooWoo 101 online course https://lisamw.vipmembervault.com/teaser/courses/view/2

## Recommended Books

* Discover Your Soul's Path Through the Akashic Records: Taking Your Life from Ordinary to ExtraOrdinary by Linda Howe

* Healing Through the Akashic Records: Using the Power of Your Sacred Wounds to Discover Your Soul's Perfection by Linda Howe

* How to Read the Akashic Records: Accessing the Archive of the Soul and Its Journey by Linda Howe

* Opening to Channel: How to Connect with Your Guide by Sanaya Roman and Duane Packer

## Recommended Websites

* Chalice Well Trust Gardens http://www.chalicewell.org.uk/

* Forest Bathing and Nature Therapy Meetup https://www.meetup.com/Forest-Bathing-and-Nature-Therapy/

* Geocaching https://www.geocaching.com/play

* Megalithic: for sacred wells and sites in the UK https://www.megalithic.co.uk/index.php

* Peper Harow http://www.peperharow.info/

* Weekly Messages from your Record Keepers with Vickie Young https://www.medicinedreamhealing.com/my-weekly-messages/

* The Order of Bards, Ovates & Druids https://www.druidry.org/

* Anima Monday, a blog about animism https://animamonday.wordpress.com/

# Learn More

If you'd like to further the development of your relationship with yourself by connecting with Nature, I'd love to help you with this! Please my website to learn more: **http://hollyworton.com**. That's also the best place to find my latest blog posts and podcast episodes.

My primary way of supporting people at this time is through Patreon. By joining my online community there, you can receive the benefits of my done-for-you mindset work, get discounts on one-to-one sessions with me, and get free tickets to my guided Nature walks: **https://www.patreon.com/hollyworton**.

I occasionally run guided walks in Surrey, and I have also organized what I call woodland experience days, where I take groups out into Nature to meditate and connect with the trees. I will also be planning a series of walks that include visits to some of the trees in this book. Information on all of my events can be found on my website: **http://hollyworton.com**. Admission to my walks is free for my Patrons at certain tiers.

# About the Author

Holly Worton is an author and podcaster who helps people connect with themselves through connecting with Nature. She enjoys spending time outdoors in Nature, walking long-distance trails and exploring Britain's sacred sites. Holly is originally from California and now lives in the Surrey Hills, but has also lived in Spain, Costa Rica, Mexico, Chile, and Argentina. She is a member of the Druid order OBOD.

You can find her podcast on Apple Podcasts, or wherever you listen to podcasts. Links to subscribe, as well as the full list of episodes, can be found here: **http://www.hollyworton.com/podcast**.

You can join her online community where you can receive the benefits of her done-for-you mindset work, and also get discounts on one-to-one sessions, by joining her on Patreon: **https://www.patreon.com/hollyworton**.

You can find her other books, including her books on walking long-distance trails and business mindset, wherever you purchased this book.

Finally, you can stay in touch by subscribing to her newsletter on her main website: **http://www.hollyworton.com**.

# About the Designer

Esther Lemmens is a visual arts lover, book and word addict, course junkie, ethical eco-warrior, organic foodie, green tea connoisseur, holistic health geek, professional pedant and crazy cat lady, with a zest for life!

She moved to the UK from the Netherlands in 1999 and has been running her graphic design business from Norwich ever since.

Being a multi-passionate business rebel with a cause, her Zesty brand is ever evolving. Through Zesty Books, she loves helping unconventional authors to visually bring their books to life.

You can find her on **www.zestybooks.co.uk** or **www.zesty.me**.

# Also by Holly Worton

**Nature books**

* If Trees Could Talk: Life Lessons from the Wisdom of the Woods

**Walking books**

* Alone on the South Downs Way: One Woman's Solo Journey from Winchester to Eastbourne
* Walking the Downs Link: Planning Guide & Reflections on Walking from St. Martha's Hill to Shoreham-by-Sea
* Alone on the Ridgeway: One Woman's Solo Journey from Avebury to Ivinghoe Beacon
* Walking the Wey-South Path: Planning Guide & Reflections on Walking from Guildford to Amberley

**Business books**

* Business Beliefs: 600+ Beliefs That Make Up a Successful Business Mindset
* Business Blocks: How to Identify and Release Your Blocks to Create a Successful Business Mindset
* Business Visibility: How to Transform Your Business Mindset & Increase Your Visibility
* Business Intuition: Learn to Tap Into Your Intuition for Easy Business Success

# A Request

If you enjoyed this book, please review it online. It takes just a couple of minutes to write a quick review. It would mean the world to me! Good reviews help other readers to discover new books.

Thank you, thank you, thank you.

Made in the USA
Monee, IL
18 November 2022

18068920R00129